FANTASTIC PEOPLE

Published in the United States by Galahad Books, a division of
A & W Publishers, Inc., 95 Madison Avenue, New York, New York 10016
Originally published in England by Pierrot Publishing Limited, London

Copyright: Text: Pierrot Publishing Limited 1980
Copyright: Illustrations: Various (see Acknowledgements page)

ISBN 0 88365 464 4
LCCN 80 67572

Designed by Julie Harris & Steve Ridgeway
Assisted by Jill Gambold
Production by Book Production Consultants, Cambridge, UK
Typesetting by Expression Typesetters, London
Color separation by Anglia Reproductions Ltd, Witham, Essex, UK
Printed & bound by Toppan Printing Co Ltd, Singapore

First American edition

FANTASTIC PEOPLE

ALLAN SCOTT
AND
MICHAEL SCOTT ROHAN

Galahad Books • New York City

Dedication

For Rob Holdstock, Chris Carlsen, Robert Black, and all the rest – to whom we owe so much.

All the fantastic people in this book are unfortunately genuine, with the exception of the authors (and other humans) who are figments of a diseased imagination.

CONTENTS

IN THE BEGINNING...

Somewhere in the depths of the oldest memories of our race, a swirling source of dreams and madness, lingers a presence that still touches the borders of the everyday world: a memory of the secret peoples. In myth and legend, fairytale and folklore, they live on, sometimes shrunken, sometimes grotesque, yet always with an aura of unique power. And the memory is tinged with ancient wonder – and fear.

It was not always a memory.

There was a time, long ago, when the elder races – the Children of Cain, as they are called in the Book of Genesis – were a force on the earth more powerful than man has ever been. A power lived in them that

IN THE BEGINNING . . . was the golden age, when elementals and human beings lived side by side, in harmony. For hundreds, perhaps thousands of years, the titan nursed infant humanity out of the stone age to its new birth in the age of metals. Numenos' lost valley, in an untraceable corner of Greece, managed to preserve that golden age for centuries after the defeat and scattering of the titans. Now it is lost to us for all time, except in legends and echoes of the past.

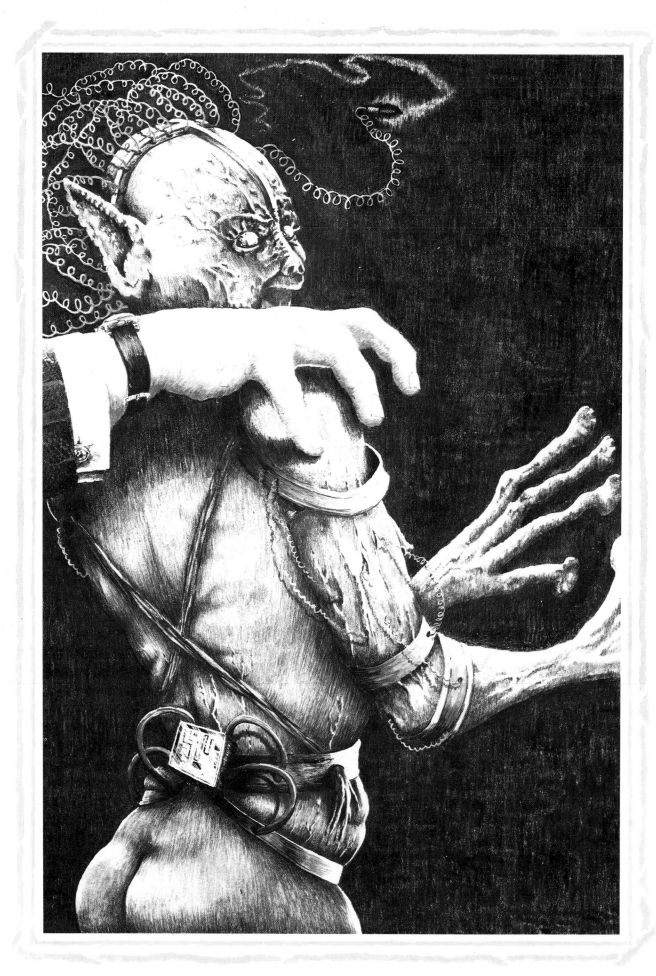

made them at once more and less than human; we have a confused recollection of it that we call magic. Thousands of years before primitive men learned the first laborious techniques for extracting and using metals, these magical races had a civilisation that far outstripped science and technology. It ranged far and wide, into worlds and dimensions of existence now closed to the living for all eternity, and endured longer than the whole of recorded human history. Yet today hardly a trace of it remains.

How can this be possible? How could such awesome beings fail to scar the planet they lived on with the traces of their birth, their life, and their death? Why is it that archaeologists and palaeontologists never come across their relics and remains among all the other debris of long-departed lifeforms? The last question is the easiest to answer. Occasionally – *very* occasionally – they do; but until now they have not been able to recognise them. It is not too hard to see why. If you found, say, a wrist-watch in a layer of early Roman pottery – or, more startlingly, in a layer of dinosaur bones – would you stop to consider whether Romans or dinosaurs wore watches? Not without some other reason. Far easier to assume that someone else had dug there before you, and lost his watch. Of course, if you examined it closely you might just find that it operated on the ancient Roman calendar, or was made to fit an entirely unhuman wrist. But (assuming you were a conscientious excavator) would you bother to take a second look? Especially if you were more than a little afraid of the answer . . . And it is very rare to find anything as recognisable as a wrist-watch; the elder races depended far less on material things than we do. Besides, few of *ours* survive long. We have very few genuine ancient Greek statues, compared to the number that we know were made. The situation is no better with physical

Opposite: In her novel Frankenstein, *Mary Shelley put forward the idea of a form of artificial life animated by an electrical 'life force'. The evidence of the Bremen Transcript suggests that the idea is far older. It seems that even the ancient 'gods' dabbled in such experiments in their search for power.*
Overleaf: Corineus, last of the titan overlords of humanity.

remains. We know that the world was far richer and more hospitable to life in the past than it is now – thanks, in part, to ourselves – and yet the total number of lifeforms we have found as fossils is much lower than the total number alive today. Animal and plant remains are mostly destroyed by scavengers, decay, and other natural processes; left to herself Nature wastes nothing, and only by very rare accidents do recognisable traces survive.

Clearly only a tiny fraction of the past has been preserved for us, and all our knowledge of it is no more than a series of glimpses. We see only the familiar: we look for things and people not too unlike those of today, and when we find them we dismiss all else as legend. Life is more comfortable that way. But once in a while we discover something that makes us take a new look at what we once dismissed or ignored – and now we have come across the Bremen Transcript.

It could be a forgery, of course, like the Vinland Map that showed the Viking discovery of America, centuries before Columbus. But that is just what the Vikings *did* do, as we have since discovered: the Vinland Map was a forged record of a true event. That could be the case with the Transcript, as well.

But it is hard to see how it *could* have been forged, and harder still to see why. It was discovered quite by accident when archaeologists were excavating a small site beside the historic medieval monastery in the city of Bremen in North Germany, not far from Hamburg and the border with Denmark. It had been deliberately buried, in a wax-sealed wooden chest, some ten feet below the then ground-level. With it were other and more evidently valuable things. It was wrapped in a length of coarse silk, perhaps an altarcloth. This was probably Chinese in origin: it would have been brought from Canton to Baghdad by Arab traders, and from there Viking merchants would have taken it across Russia to one of the great Scandinavian merchant towns such as Hedeby in Denmark – not that far from Bremen. The package was wrapped again in a coarse linen shirt, and tucked inside a casket made of bone and trimmed with gold. This looks as though it was originally a reliquary (a container for religious relics), probably made in Ireland, another Viking trade centre. The careful packaging and the sealed box have preserved the manuscript fairly well, although the ink has tended to eat through the paper in places. On-the-spot conservation work by an expert from the local records office saved most of the text in these areas, but several leaves must already have been missing from the manuscript when it was buried. Those that remain contain two main texts. The first purports to be a Latin translation of a Greek text by a writer named only as *Numenos*. The surviving portion deals, to begin with at least, with the topic of animal and plant life in southern Greece. This suggests that the owner could not have been the author: a monk from Bremen would have been unlikely to travel so far afield, even on pilgrimage. But then, without a break, the manuscript suddenly launches into a very different sort of account. The first warning of this significant change of direction comes at the head of a folio sheet that unfortunately suffered damage at some time before the manuscript was hidden. It begins in the middle of a sentence:

'. . . conflict between the people of the woods and the glade-dancers. He said that once there had been those who would have ended such conflict the hour it began, but when the *ephor* questioned him he would not speak of it further, but said that all knew well enough that such matters were now decided by Corineus.

'I enquired of the *ephor* who this Corineus might be, wondering whether it was he that I had seen on the mountainside. The *ephor* was at first unwilling to speak of it further, but when he understood that I would have the truth, he told me that Corineus was of the ancient stock of the titans, that he knew much, and that until the arrival of the stranger, Corineus had cared for justice and peace between the village and the other peoples of the valley. But the *ephor* was no longer certain what might come about in these matters, since none knew the race of the stranger.'

Earlier sections of the transcript make it clear that Numenos usually began his researches by asking the village elder, the *ephor*, if he knew of any noteworthy beasts or plants to be found in the area. Here it seems that Numenos has already caught a glimpse of several unusual beings: the mysterious Corineus, said to be 'of the ancient stock of the titans', and others which he does not specify in the surviving text. Not averse to a little guile, he makes further enquiries:

'I thought at first to ask him about such creatures as I had seen in the valley, and never before in all my travels. But thinking better of this I feigned to have seen such creatures on occasion in the woodlands about my home, though, so I maintained, they would not traffic with our people, and we knew but little of them. At this the *ephor* seemed pleased, saying that it was evident we knew little of how to approach the elder races, and that such was the common way of mankind in these degenerate days. Many of them, he said, still lived upon the most amiable of terms with his people, because of the wisdom of himself, his father, his grandfather, and all the *ephors* before them, who cultivated their acquaintance and refrained from needlessly offending them. He told me that according to Corineus there had been many such races, but these had been harried by man until they had left the lands they shared with him, seeking out places so far distant that he might never travel there. I resolved to press the *ephor* to relate these tales, since it seemed he could by flattery be led to boast of his knowledge. But for the moment I spoke to him only of the creatures of his own valley.'

Numenos does not go into great detail about what the *ephor* told him; his appetite now seems thoroughly whetted. Instead, he decides to seek out these mysterious 'peoples of the valley' for himself. Again, the head of the folio is damaged:

'. . . made my way over the brow of the hill and descended the steep slope. Here I made my way stumblingly through numerous bushes growing amidst olive trees in a place that was surely at some time a cultivated grove. The people of the village had ceased to till this side of the hill, though by day I later found it had more sun than the other, so I

Overleaf: The world is rich in travellers' tales of dragons, giants, sea-monsters, and 'fabulous beasts'. Legends of this kind sprang up around many of the great voyages of exploration in the 15th and 16th centuries. The evidence of the Transcript suggests that some of these stories may be true.

deduced this must be a part of their treaty with Corineus. The terrain was difficult, and I mislaid one of my sandals when its strap was severed by a sharp rock. Fearing snakes, if nothing worse, I moved forward with the greatest caution, going by the clearest way but keeping always to the shadows of the trees, for the moon was full and gave good light but deep shade. Soon thereafter I heard the sound of waters, and came to a place where a small river flowed over a precipitous part of the hill into a wide, still pool below. From where I stood, half-concealed by a large boulder, I could discern many figures gathered about the water, or plunging into its depths, and above the sound of the waterfall I was able to distinguish the sounds of voices and much merriment, with the music of pipes and other instruments. Many of these voices I took by their sound to be those of women; I determined to find a more commanding viewpoint so that I might confirm my judgement. It seemed to me that the *ephor* with his tales of the valley might be seeking to cloak the practices of some mystery cult, and deter me from seeing what could be seen. Yet the moonlight was sufficiently clear that I soon perceived many of the figures to be most curiously shaped about the legs, which had the appearance of being covered with thick hair most like to a goat's. These danced and capered continuously, and seemed most mirthful.

'The women in the pool appeared most delightfully formed, and most graceful in their motions, yet I could not calculate how many of them there might be, since at one time there would be no more than one or two in the water, and at others perhaps a dozen. They wore no clothing, but their hair was long and sleek. Along the edge of the pool perhaps eight or nine other women were sporting. Often these delightful creatures would sit with their long and comely legs dangling in the pool, yet they would not swim, and after a short while one or another of the hairy men would seize them and hurl them back into the circle of dancers just beyond. After a short while the dance grew more furious yet, and a number of the shaggy men who had no womenfolk leaped into the pool with many shouts and gestures. The women there (if women they were, for their skins glistened with a lustre as of scales, and they swam and dived with great freedom) shrieked most lamentably at this intrusion, yet, once caught, laughed and sported without fear.

'I resolved to look more closely into this matter, since I observed that the other dancers were also engaged in a new sport, and I felt it my duty to discover all I could of these strange creatures and their habits; yet at that moment, becoming aware of a sound behind me, I turned my head and observed that the rock where I had taken my first view of the pool appeared in motion. Fearing to be crushed, I sought the shelter of the nearest olive trees at once; and only then, espying from my new place of concealment, could I discern that this was no boulder but a living creature that walked upon two legs. It was perhaps twice the height of a full-grown man, and its head was like no other I had ever seen, namely half-man and half-beast. I had no doubt that it was this figure I had observed on the first day, and that this was none other than Corineus the titan himself. And now I knew without doubt or debate that this was one of those creatures condemned by father Zeus to the grim fires of Tartarus in the golden age that the scholars say preceded our own, countless years ago.'

Numenos, now thoroughly frightened, makes his way back to the village. The following day he continues to question the *ephor*, but is now clearly aware of the fact that what he has seen is an enclave of non-human races that have somehow avoided the Great Retreat already hinted at by the *ephor*. Over several days he manages to extract a fragmentary and sometimes confusing account of a whole series of races apparently rooted in a quite different order of creation from our own. That account, making up the greater part of the Bremen Transcript, has been the major source of our text. Using it together with the hints offered by myth, legend, and folklore the world over, it is possible to reconstruct, in outline at least, the history of the secret peoples.

One final piece of evidence remains: the second text, no more than a single leaf bound into the manuscript. It is in a different, much coarser hand, and may well be the work of another monk at the same monastery some hundred years later. The account this time is in Middle High German, but phrased in the dry, laconic style characteristic of the Norse sagas. Some idiomatic quirks suggest that it has in fact been translated rather roughly from an Old Norse text. The tale certainly concerns Scandinavians, apparently from the early Viking period of the 8th or 9th century, the crew of a longship captained by a man called Thorgrim Alfvinnsson. His name, and those others mentioned, give no clue as to their country of origin; most likely they were Norwegians, or possibly early Icelanders. Enough of the context is left to suggest a place somewhere in the Mediterranean:

'. . . ten days sailing past many small islands, some green, but most

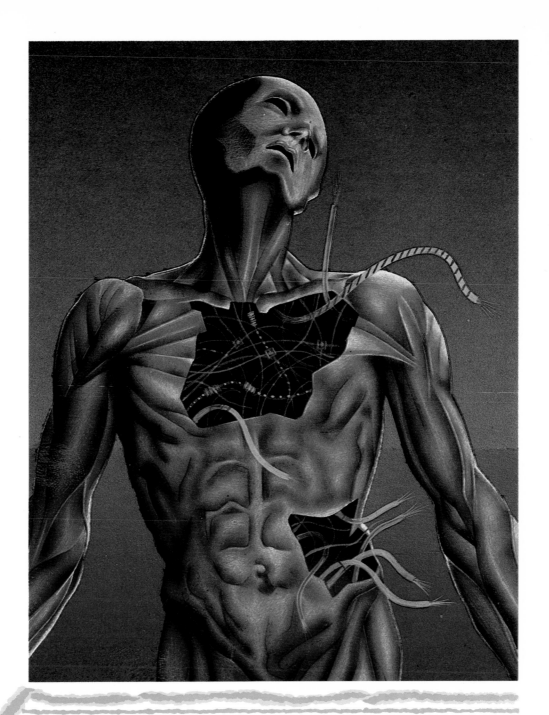

fit only for goats, they landed at a place where there were good beaches to repair their ship. Then Yngvi Gudleifsson goes into the woods to find timber, and a short while later comes running out again without his axe. Thorgrim asks him what the matter is, and he says that there are better

Above: Early attempts by the elementals to take on physical shape were often disastrous failures. The most successful experiments were carried out by the earth elementals, who modelled their bodies on the human form, but in the process more than one of them threw away the gift of immortal life. Opposite: Avram, a titan craftsman cast off by a fleeing trading ship, clutches a copper speculum majorum *stolen from his god-master. The speculum, used in the magical art of divination, required the craftsmanship that was the speciality of the titans. Not surprisingly, the war between titans and gods set the elemental arts of magic back by several centuries.*

places to cut trees than that one. And then Yngvi falls dead. Then Thorgrim and five others went up into the woods with their weapons. They saw there men with cloaks of leaves and green skins, who ran from them, and then they met with a creature as tall as the mast of their ship, with a great club. The giant broke open the skull of Berse Oyster [*a nickname*] so the brains flew everywhere, but Thorgrim cut its hamstrings with his halberd, and after that there was little fight in the giant. A little afterwards they found the place where Yngvi had left his axe, and there was a woman lying there dead, with her feet cut from her legs. Then there were few of Thorgrim's men who wished to stay in the woods. Thorgrim argued with them, but he could not stop them, and they went back to the ship. As they sailed away sea-wights in the shape of beautiful women followed their wake, calling to the men. Tryggvi Bjarnarsson leapt overboard to meet them, and was drowned.

'After this Thorgrim steered a course to the south, and the next day he came upon a ship of the dark men, and fought them, and made great slaughter . . .'

The story goes on to become a conventional tale of piracy and murder in the true Viking style – and no further reference is made to that mysterious landing-place. Was it the same village that Numenos visited? Someone must have thought so, to take such trouble to bind the accounts together. Or perhaps there was more than one enclave left behind after the Great Retreat? Whatever the truth of the matter, one thing is established beyond doubt. The two manuscripts of the Bremen Transcript prove that a few remnants of the secret races survived into our own recorded history, and left behind enough of the truth about themselves to allow us a glimpse into a time beyond the dawn of humanity. Much detailed and scholarly work remains to be done on the Transcript; our intention here has been to give the reader an understanding of the extraordinary new perspectives into our history, palaeontology, and mythology that it opens up. Here, as far as we can restore it, is the history of the secret races: the most fantastic people this planet has ever seen.

GODS, TITANS, AND DRAGONS

Most of the world's great mythologies speak of the time before creation as one of darkness and chaos, when element clashed with element and the universe was a place without form or order. The Bremen Transcript makes it clear that what we are seeing in the dark and roiling clouds of these ancestral stories is the coming of the elementals.

It seems that all the magical races can trace their origins back to the elementals, those creatures, more spirit than substance, that drew their life from earth, air, fire, and water. The first forms of elemental life must have started their climb up the ladder of evolution at about the same time as the first primeval life-cell began moving in the waters of Pre-

Stories from every part of the known world speak of the long years of chaos in the dark time before recorded history when the elementals began their first experiments with physical bodies. The forms they took were often bizarre and frightening, attempts by creatures unused to fleshly limitations to express the power and fluidity of their elemental state. Those huge and terrifying forms still haunt the depths of our racial memory today.

Cambrian earth. But the two types of life knew nothing of one another's existence. Life as we know it exists in three dimensions of space and one of time. But elemental life, although it knows all these dimensions, derives most of its strength from another: perhaps the Nirvana spoken of in the eastern religions. Apparently the early elementals, like the dinosaurs, were too preoccupied with their own affairs to pay much attention to anything else. But as they developed the first glimmerings of intelligence, they began to realise that theirs was far from being the only thinking life-form. They saw the first tribes of ape-men learning to manipulate the world around them with hand and brain; and although the elementals were capable of manipulating our dimensions by what we would regard as magic, they envied – and feared – the physical power of primitive man. It would seem that they began their struggle to adopt physical shape out of jealousy and fright – hardly very high motives for beings who would later describe themselves as gods.

Their first attempts were clumsy in the extreme. The problem was that the elementals regarded flesh – protoplasm – as something too weak and too needlessly complex to suit their requirements. Instead they tried to sculpt themselves bodies out of the elements they were most at home in, or out of things native to those elements. It was not a simple process. The earth elementals had the easiest task, but the rest found that even with the aid of magic a physical body was a devilishly tricky thing to hold together. The giant Ymir, father of the Norse gods and giants, was supposed to have been born out of a mixture made from the mists and ice of Niflheim and the fires of Muspellheim. Legend speaks of his body being torn to pieces by his grandsons, the gods, but it is more likely that he simply fell apart. Later his bones were used to build mountains, so Ymir must have put some earth in the mix, as well as water and fire.

This kind of elemental alliance was really a step up from the earliest and most disastrous efforts that have left the image of Chaos firmly embedded in our racial consciousness. In fact it did achieve some measure of success. In Egyptian myth no fewer than eight elementals are named as joint creators of the world. In Assyrian myth two stable life-forms emerge from Tiamat, the sea, and father Anshar, the heavens, and Kishar, the earth. The Greeks speak of Gaia, the earth, and Uranus, the heavens, as the begetters of the gods: clearly we are seeing a memory of embodied earth and sky elementals. But the process lacked refinement, and in the last analysis most of the more successful elementals were forced to turn to some kind of flesh for their earthly incarnations. A few of the earth-spirits, seeing greater strength and life in the plant world, tried to animate trees, and in this way the first of the green people were born. But the large and powerful earth elementals that took human or humanoid shapes had the earliest successes.

By all accounts the first of them to win through to our dimension were hardly worth the trouble. They spent most of their time fighting and mutilating one another, and caused immense amounts of damage all over the planet. Many of the massive geological changes that we imagine to have taken millions of years were probably the work of a day or two for these magical armies, and it is hardly surprising that this early chaos is reflected once again in legends the world over. But in due

Above: The titan-dragon Fafnir dies by the sword of the hero Siegfried: an illustration by Arthur Rackham for Wagner's operatic cycle The Ring of the Nibelungs. *Over the centuries the original version of the story, in which an unheroic, greedy, and rather sly Siegfried murders the unsuspecting dragon, has been completely transformed. The Siegfried story is only one of many similar dragon-slaying tales, and in each case the most recent version of the story casts the dragon as the villain. There is some truth in this: certainly many of the titan-dragons were guilty of gold-lust, and in their old age many of them lost their human qualities and became indistinguishable from reptilian dragons. But few of them attacked human beings without provocation: and none of them ever demanded human sacrifice.*

Opposite and Above: Despite the ancient friendship between titans and humanity, human heroes took a very active part in the Second Titan War. One of the creators of Typhon, a titan-magician named Gigas, was tracked down to his skilfully concealed stronghold by one of his own pupils, Kilvath. Master and pupil confronted each other for a few seconds, hesitating to begin the fight.

course the forces of natural selection ensured that the least successful specimens were destroyed, buried, blasted into their component parts, or otherwise disposed of, and three races emerged from the dust of combat with their immense physical powers set in complete harmony with their native 'magical' talents: the gods, the titans, and the cyclopes, or one-eyed giants. The cyclopes and the titans survived because of their dexterity, and their skill in making tools and weapons. The gods survived because they had refined their native elemental powers to work in their new environment. Together, the three new races looked set fair for a happy future, with the cyclopes and titans acting as the labourers of the new order. We hear of their work on Mount Olympus, and later on the walls of Troy, while the story of the giant stonemason who built the fortresses of Asgard is famous. But the gods were bad managers, and made a speciality of welching on their contracts. In return for his work on the walls of Asgard, the titan mason had quite literally been promised the moon – not to mention the hand of the alluring goddess of fertility, Freyja. But in the event the cunning god Loki transformed himself into a mare and lured away the titan's magical stallion, Svadilfari, so preventing him from fulfilling his agreement. When, not unnaturally, the titan complained of his treatment, the thunder-god Thor smashed his skull.

Under the circumstances it is hardly surprising that the titans and the cyclopes chose to declare war. Unfortunately they stood little chance against the gods, who were very skilled in magic despite their poor grasp of labour relations. The weapons that the titans themselves had forged were turned against them, and to deadly effect. Their leaders were banished to the narrow confines of a dimension known to the Greeks as Tartarus, to the Norse as Niflheim, and to the Hebrews as Sheol. But the gods could not afford to exterminate the titans, so they

Opposite: Before the Titan Wars, the relationship between titans and human beings was often very close. The story of Prometheus suggests that titan smiths and metalworkers gave human beings their first instruction in the skills that eventually brought us out of the stone age at the dawn of our civilisation. Overleaf: According to Greek legend, many of the gods adopted semi-human form in an attempt to conceal themselves from Typhon and his creators during the second Titan War. This, it was said, was why the Egyptians portrayed the gods with the heads of animals. It seems more likely that the figures they saw were the grotesque members of an elemental alliance against the titans.

enslaved them instead – a mistake that would be made again, thousands of years later, by the Romans.

The titans, with the earth element dominant in their make-up, had always been interested in digging. At first this may have been purely for medical reasons: titans drew most of their strength from contact with the earth, and during battles in their prehistory, many of them would 'dig themselves in' to recover from their wounds. Greek legend records how Hercules was able to kill the titan Antaeus by lifting him into the air, where he could win no strength from his element, and then throttling him. However, the titans became very interested in the gemstones and the metal ores they found in the earth, and as their skills grew they became adept in metalworking, tool-making, and jewel-cutting. Soon the titan miners were producing beautiful weapons, jewellery, and trinkets: things treasured by primitive man. The gods, aware as always that these half-apes might be useful allies for the resentful titans, forbade them to teach human beings any but the most basic crafts. But the rule could not be enforced, and one titan, Prometheus, was able to teach his pupils almost everything he knew before he was captured and barbarically punished by the leader of the gods, Zeus. Prometheus was chained to a mountainside on the Caucasus, and each day an eagle would swoop from the skies to tear out his liver. Each night his grisly wounds would be magically healed, in readiness for the next day's torment.

The Prometheus incident was the signal for the beginning of the second Titan war. Unknown to the gods, a number of the titans had been perfecting their own magical skills and now they unleashed their work on a terrified world. The astonished gods were confronted by the most monstrous being that has ever walked on the face of the earth: Typhon the terrible. Legend speaks of him as having a hundred heads, some of them the heads of beasts, some of ogres, some modelled after the human form. Nests of limbs grew from his massive trunk, and his legs could bestride a mountain.

It seems very likely that the titan-magicians had been helped in the creation of Typhon by some of the more sophisticated elementals, who found the arrogant new power of the gods more than a little disturbing. Certainly Typhon must have been more than flesh: nothing so huge could ever have existed entirely in the natural world, and he was almost invulnerable. Indian legend records that Typhon – or Ravana as they called him – was a presentable enough figure when he first appeared; but although he could not be killed by the weapons and magic of the gods, their constant bombardment eventually criss-crossed his body with hideous scars and weals. The Egyptians remember him, too, as Set the evil one, though obviously they never saw him in the flesh since they seem to have forgotten his size.

Although Typhon kept most of the gods very busy, they did not forget the risk of an alliance with the humans. The stories of a great flood at about this time can be traced to places as far apart as Alaska and Palestine. With this flood the gods hoped to minimize the danger from the mortal races, and also to flush out the deeper haunts of the titans and their allies. Serene in their mountain fastnesses, they could afford to watch the devastation below them and laugh.

They had the overenthusiastic support of a group of water elementals led by Poseidon, the god of the sea. He seems to have been an ally of Zeus, despite their continual disagreements; Greek legend suggests that they were brothers, and even that Hades, the air elemental who ruled the kingdom of ghosts and ghouls, was another from the same stable.

The titan revolt failed because the titans had relied too heavily on human support. What neither gods nor titans had realised was that the humans were as horrified by Typhon as anyone else. Human heroes, appalled at the destruction, turned against their mentors, and before long the titan forces were routed. The battle with Typhon himself was long and savage, and at one point the gods were forced to flee into Egypt, where they disguised themselves in semi-human form, taking the heads and attributes of wild beasts. But at the last even Typhon's strength was worn down by the interminable war, and in a final encounter Zeus was able to pin him beneath Mount Etna. To hold the allegiance of their new allies, the gods explained that the floods released against mankind were intended to wipe out the evil they had seen growing in its midst. By definition the survivors were therefore among the virtuous, and need fear no further retribution.

This time the defeated titans did not stay behind to meet their fate.

Many fled to the outer reaches of the world: the lands of ice and frost to north and south, known to the Vikings as Jotunheim. There they plot in secret, preparing for the last great uprising which is yet to come, on a day known to northern seers as the Ragnarok, when all creation will return once again to the primal chaos of the battling elementals. If that day ever dawns, it will be through the greed and folly of a race that thought of themselves as gods.

But in their exile, the titan race decayed. Many of their finest leaders and craftsmen had disappeared during the wars with the gods, and by degrees the survivors of the race regressed, until most were as brutal and stupid as their distant ancestors. The few that found their way down into Europe in the course of the centuries were foolish, ungainly, and greedy for gold: so the old titan love of precious things was perverted into treasure-lust. Far from protecting mankind, these sad and decayed creatures would often feed on human flesh. Such mindless ogres were fit victims for mortal heroes like Jack the Giant-killer, and it

Left: A typical human interpretation of the Jack-and-the-Beanstalk legend, which actually seems to have been based on an incident in the Second Titan War, when the humans turned on their former allies. The Titan Cormran seems to have been a reasonably peaceful and benevolent fellow, interested chiefly in genetics. The goose that laid golden eggs is said to have been one of his early successes; instances of the recessive gene that led to it have continued to pop up through the ages, the latest documented by the eminent biochemist Dr. Adolphus Spraag. He was engaged in breeding giant food plants to assist the growth of human agriculture when humans looking for plunder stormed his laboratory and killed him. The story later became attached to that of the hero Jack, killer of a degenerate ogre that briefly terrorized southwest England.

51

is hardly surprising that the Viking myth-makers mocked them as cowards and fools. A favourite Viking tale speaks of the god Thor's fishing-trip with the giant Hymir. From the very start Thor rowed the boat out far further than Hymir had ever been before, and then baited his hook with the head of one of Hymir's oxen. For long hours he played the line, while the open sea around their boat grew ever more stormy. Then, suddenly, Thor felt an enormous tug on the line. He hauled back on it with such strength that his feet broke through the planking of the boat, and as Hymir desperately bailed, an enormous head broke the surface, straining at the end of Thor's line. It was Jormungand, the

Opposite: Various mythologies make it clear that the gods were utterly unscrupulous in their dealings both with humans and with fellow elementals. Ares, Greek god of war, and his Norse counterpart Odin delighted in whipping up bloodthirsty struggles among their worshippers. They would even join in to cause a favourite, or an over-successful, warrior to be killed, behaving like Roman Emperors at a gladiatorial display.

Midgard Serpent, whose body encircles the whole Outer Ocean, and at the sight Hymir cried out and cut the line. Weakened by his trial of

Above: Boreas, the North Wind, a powerful air elemental. Opposite: the gods Odin (back) and Loki (left) confront the shape-shifting dwarf Alberich, who has taken the form of a dragon. Alberich had stolen the Rhinegold, and the two gods intended to take it from him to pay the titan mason who had built Valhalla.

strength with the serpent, Thor struck out at Hymir, knocking him senseless. At any other time he would have killed the giant outright. But was it only fright that made Hymir cut the line, or did he know more about Jormungand than Thor?

Hymir may have known that a few of the titan-magicians who had helped in the creation of Typhon had survived the war. By their great arts they managed to conceal themselves from the hunting gods in the depths of the earth, in the dimensions beyond those we know, or in some cases by imitating the shape and nature of earthly creatures. Of these, Jormungand was one; and he was not alone. Other titans had also taken the form of dragons, but kept their magical powers even in their new bodies. As a result, the titan-dragons became some of the most formidable creatures to survive into recorded history. They were all but immortal, possessed of terrible physical and magical weapons, almost invulnerable, and at the last so steeped in their own love of gold that they forgot they had ever been more than dragons. Once again the titan love of skilled manual work was perverted into a lust that brought them down in raging fire on the treasure-houses of the rising mortal races. These were the great dragons of myth and legend, who guarded the richest treasures of the world: the Golden Fleece of Colchis, the golden apples of the Hesperides, the Rhinegold, the great Baltic hoard, and many others that have not been so clearly recorded. But the passage of time dulled the edge of their greed even as it dulled their memories, and by about the seventh century AD most of the dragons still alive were content to sit peacefully on their hoards and indulge in meditation and the study of philosophy – with the occasional good meal to add a little spice to their existence. They found human flesh very pleasant, but not exceptionally so, and rarely worth the trouble of hunting. However, when the local peasantry took to worshipping them, and offering them nubile virgins for sacrifice, they did not turn aside from a pleasurable meal. If human beings wished to make life easier for them, then that was well, but no concern of theirs. When well-armed heroes eventually arrived to despatch them to Nirvana, many of them probably died without the least idea of why they were being killed, or even why the local community had taken to supplying them with free snacks in the first place.

A number of the titan-dragons who adopted winged forms were able to escape even further afield. One, known to the Indians of Mexico as Quetzlcoatl, established himself as a local god before he was discovered and driven out by the established gods. He is still remembered for all the attributes of a true titan, including his love of the arts and of metallurgy. In China and Japan the flight of dragons was observed, though neither country suffered greatly from dragon spoliation. There it seems likely that the fleeing titans established an alliance with some disaffected water elementals, since throughout the east the dragon is believed to have control of the rain, and is invoked in

Overleaf: The titan-dragons are constantly portrayed in myth and legend as robbers, hoarders of treasure, and merciless exploiters of human fear. But evidence in the transcript suggests that even in their reptilian form many of the titans remained close to the friends they had made among humanity before the Titan Wars. One Transcript story, put into the mouth of Corineus, even speaks of a titan-dragon rescuing a young Phoenician trader, Daveh, and his Egyptian bride, H'as-el-net, from shipwreck in a violent Mediterranean storm. Daveh had met his bride in Crete and was bringing her home to his people when the storm struck. He had abandoned all hope when he heard the dragon's unmistakable cry. Its magic had warned it of Daveh's peril, and it had flown halfway across the Middle Sea to save him.

times of flood and drought.

In Europe, however, the surviving dragons were hunted down and slaughtered by human beings with no memory or understanding of what the original titans had tried to do for them. The dragon of the Baltic hoard was killed by the hero Beowulf: by pure irony he died from a wound inflicted by a sword he had helped to forge himself. The dragon Fafnir, a generally peacable creature who lived by himself, miles from anywhere, in the middle of a forest, was hunted down and killed in a remarkably cowardly and underhand fashion by the brutal saga-hero Siegfried. Siegfried dug a pit on Fafnir's usual path to the nearby stream, hid there, and cut open the dragon's soft belly as it passed in innocent unconcern on its way to the water. Siegfried was mainly interested in the Rhinegold, which Fafnir was guarding, and was too stupid to realise that the dragon's blood conferred several magical advantages on anyone who drank it. Unfortunately he chanced to burn his finger and lick it while roasting chunks of the dragon's heart for someone else: he thus picked up a fool's portion of magical knowledge that allowed him to upset most of the established society in the Rhine area. Before he could do too much damage, however, he was despatched by the well-aimed spear of his enemy Hagen.

One of the last surviving dragons provided the ancient world with its most potent offensive weapon: Greek fire, invented after scientists in the city of Byzantium dissected its freshly-killed corpse. And so a flame born in the workshops of the titans, a flame that had been employed to deadly effect in the second Titan war, was used for some 800 years as a seagoing weapon. The secret was finally lost to mankind when a horde of plundering Crusaders set light to large areas of Byzantium, including the fire-vats, in the year 1204.

TROLLS

From the account given in the Bremen Transcript, trolls, or trows, seem to be cast in the role of clown princes of the titan stock, despite the fact that their line of descent from the original titans is much the same as that of the vicious giants and ogres that plagued early medieval Europe. The authority for this is Corineus the titan himself, who spent many years among troll-tribes in the north before his return to Greece. In a surprisingly detailed narrative, the *ephor* relates the titan's story to Numenos. Apparently, he says, the reputation of trolls as sinister creatures is ill-deserved. Indeed, they are a remarkably stay-at-home race, probably because their chances for travel are strictly limited by the

The image of trolls preserved in Scandinavian folk-tale and legend leaves us with an impression of large, ugly, stupid, but essentially good-natured characters much maligned by later writers. This particular troll shows all the outsize features of his breed: feet, hands, and all of his three noses are built on a truly magnificent scale. But he is quite content to sink into a peaceful, if noisy, sleep while his human companion keeps watch.

fact that daylight usually makes them very uncomfortable. However, they are able to endure it provided it finds them in shady woods or heavy undergrowth, and only the weakest of them are actually paralysed by it.

Trolls vary enormously in size. Some are as big as small giants, others are no bigger than dwarves, but all are grotesque in the extreme. Most have long noses, long ears, big, clumsy hands, flat feet, and long arms with knuckles that trail along the ground. Trolls have a primitive sense of humour: they will happily throw rocks at anything that moves for hours on end, and laugh hysterically if, by some freakish coincidence, they actually manage to hit something. For this reason if no other they are not popular with other woodland creatures, who tend to give their regular haunts the widest possible berth. This may be why men regard them as sinister creatures: it *is* rather unnerving to come across a troll in a thick wood apparently deserted by every other form of life.

Trolls find human beings altogether too smooth, regular, and handsome, but otherwise quite entertaining. Mortal women are usually far too attractive to interest male trolls – besides, their skin is not leathery enough to give a good grip – but occasionally a human woman almost ugly enough to be desirable may turn up. Generally speaking, however, they prefer their own women, who are so ugly that they very rarely show themselves above ground, preferring to remain in the troll-caves where their peculiar virtues will be properly appreciated. For this

Opposite: Grendel, an outcast even among troll-kind, conducted a twelve-year campaign of terror against the court of the Danish king Hroar, before he was literally torn apart by the hero Beowulf. Grendel was an unnatural creature who lived alone with his mother, at the heart of a huge area of marshland, guarded by dragons. Consumed by hatred and envy, this unpleasant pair soon lost what little intelligence their ancestry had given them, and became adapted to life in the marshes. The normally clownish troll physique metamorphosed into something more repellant than funny.

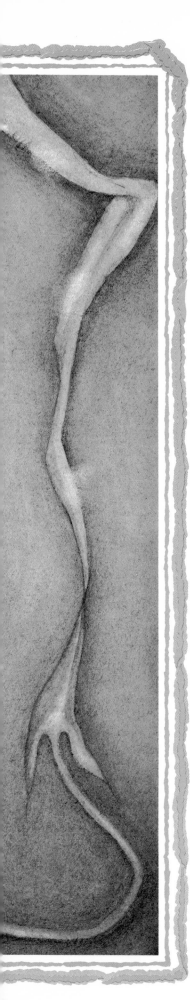

reason troll-wives tend to be either shrunken or hunch-backed, from continually bending double to negotiate low-ceilinged tunnels.

Trolls normally live in tribal groups, and will defend their territory fiercely against neighbouring tribes. However, since most of these battles take place underground, they are not often seen by human beings. Trolls dislike fire and light, so their eyes are exceptionally well-developed and, not surprisingly, they have a taste for raw meat. Despite this, and other strange and uncouth habits, they made the titan Corineus more than welcome, and he has seen no evidence of any real harm done by trolls to human beings unless one counts child-swapping.

It seems from his account that an over-handsome troll child might be foisted off on a human family, and this may account for a number of Icelandic folk-stories, among them that of the 'troll-woman's leap'. This tells of a farmer's daughter who one day turned into a troll. In fact she had been a troll all the time, but like most trolls she was none too bright, and it was only when someone happened to comment on her incredible

Left: Trolls seem to have been found in many different habitats throughout Scandinavia. Some of the larger specimens enjoyed making a nuisance of themselves by throwing rocks and trees at each other from neighbouring hilltops, but most, like this rather inoffensive character, were content to go about their business without bothering human beings at all. Though none too bright, they were able to keep their larders full by trapping and hunting small creatures such as birds and rabbits. Trolls disliked fishing, or indeed anything that involved close contact with water, such as washing. This troll, with his long, skinny arms and legs, big feet, prominent nose, long ears, and untidy tail, is typical of the smaller members of his race.

Above: A curious reference in the Thorgrimssaga Alfvinsson *describes a creature that Viking raiders encountered in North Africa. They called it a troll, after the most similar creatures in their homelands, but in fact it seems to have been something even trolls would have avoided – a ghoul, no less. Opposite: Trolls were usually happy to keep themselves to themselves, which suited everyone else. But if anyone laid hands on their tribal gold even the dimmest troll, like Geirrod could still go flaming mad.*

ugliness that she realised her true nature. At once she picked up the farmer's horse, which was standing nearby, ripped off one of its hind legs as a travelling snack, and went in search of a troll tribe rumoured to have settled nearby. However, she found her way blocked by a river, its water swelled by melting ice. Most trolls hate getting their feet wet, and she was no exception. In fury she started throwing rocks at the offending waters, until after a while it dawned on her that if she threw

enough of them she could make herself a set of stepping-stones. When she had thrown enough to cross dryshod, off she went in search of a nice, ugly troll-husband – and the island she created is still there today.

Since most troll-women were hunchbacked anyway it is quite possible that the old Norse story of Geirrod the Troll King is pure nonsense; at least, in the version commonly told. According to this story the god Thor was tricked into visiting Geirrod by Loki, who had been imprisoned by the trolls for several months. Thor took a great deal of persuading, since the gods generally regarded trolls with even less

Above: Two trolls engaged in one of their favourite sports. Since their bodies were largely made of stone, they did considerably more damage to the landscape than to each other. Opposite: A troll-wife primping herself in readiness for her marriage, with the help of some semi-human friends. Apparently troll-women were as much the slaves of fashion as many human beings.

70

favour than they regarded giants, but at last he set off. On his way he came to a river, and while he was crossing it noticed Geirrod's daughter Gialp further upstream holding a large rock. Thinking the worst, he picked up a rock himself and threw it at her. In fact, Gialp was doing her washing, but on being wooed so gracefully she naturally responded in kind, and with the usual trollish accuracy. Thor never even realised she was aiming at him, and continued on his way, determined to brook no further trouble. On reaching Geirrod's house he stumped into the entrance hall and sat down on what appeared to be a chair. Suddenly he felt himself rising towards the ceiling – not surprisingly, since he had sat on the hump of Geirrod's other daughter Greip. Thor fended off the low ceiling and climbed quickly down again. When he saw the hunchbacked troll-wife he naturally assumed he had broken her back, and stormed into Geirrod's hall in a blazing fury. Grabbing an iron bar used to hold the hall door shut at night, he flung it at the troll-king, piercing him through and through, and then turned his back on the hall and walked out. Since Geirrod was made mostly of stone, the iron rod did not bother him unduly, though it did leave a hole that he had to patch up afterwards. Trolls generally used a lime-based mortar for this. Thor always claimed that Geirrod threw the iron rod first, but then the truth would have looked bad.

The story of Thor's visit eventually reached Denmark, and in the tenth century legend has it that King Gorm of Denmark set out in search of the troll-king's palace, attracted by rumours of treasure. When he arrived he saw both Geirrod's daughters creeping about on all fours, and so assumed that the story about Thor must be true, especially when

Left: A modern image of the average troll's intelligence. Like many elementals they seemed to think that other people could, if necessary, do their thinking for them. A favourite Danish story tells of the troll who saw the moon reflected in a pool of water. Thinking it was an enormous silver coin, he climbed onto the branch of a tree overhanging the pool and reached down into the water to take his treasure. Unfortunately it seemed to be just too deep for him to reach, so he called in a couple of his friends to help him. All three climbed out onto the branch to weigh it down, and one held the first troll's feet while he tried again. At about that moment the branch, not surprisingly, snapped clean across. Since trolls cannot swim, the three treasure-hunters were not heard from again.

he noticed that most of Geirrod's navel consisted of off-colour mortar. Unfortunately many of his companions thought that the king and his daughters must have been so daunted by Thor's mighty victory that they were harmless, and proceeded to loot the troll-king's treasure-house. Now the trolls, in common with most of the titan stock, are passionately attached to their treasures, and this wanton thievery roused them to fury. Gorm and what was left of his men after the fracas were lucky to escape with their lives, and it is rumoured that the old king was so frightened that he became a Christian. If Thor could no longer kill trolls then there was little point in worshipping him.

Trolls also make an appearance in the folk-tales of the Shetlands, where they can sometimes be seen during the day, creeping about in search of shadow and shelter. Shetland trolls are said to marry only once: their wives die when the child is born, and the father dies when the child is full-grown. This may be due to a confusion between trolls and titan-dragons, who naturally had to adopt the uncomfortable reproductive methods of dragons as well as their more powerful advantages.

Troll houses could occasionally be raised on pillars when the smoke inside made the air unbreathable. This was probably a device copied from the dwarves, since it is unlikely any troll would ever think of something so sensible.

DWARVES

The Bremen Transcript has a good deal to say about a race it refers to as *Telkines*. The word seems to be a corruption of an ancient Greek name for a race related both to the titans and to the god Poseidon, and chiefly known as skilled metalworkers. But the Transcript also mentions the alternative names *pygmaies, cobolidi,* and *gnomi,* using them more or less indiscriminately. Clearly we are talking about the race known as dwarves, kobolds, or, more rarely, 'knockers'. And also, controversially, as gnomes.

Until the Transcript was discovered most linguists believed that the term 'gnome' had been coined by the sixteenth-century Swiss

Clad in human cast-offs, even an aristocratic dwarf was a pretty grotesque sight. This was a minor dwarf-leader, named something like Mog, who was on good terms with humans for a while, until he alienated them by passing bent coinage. The animal world tended to treat dwarves like the lumps of stone they very nearly were, as is happening here.

alchemist, scholar, and quack Paracelsus. In one of his works he develops a theory of elemental spirits. It is as half-baked as most of his other efforts, but close enough to the general theme of the Transcript to suggest that he might have seen a copy. If he did, it must have been a pretty quick look, but his definition of gnomes manages to be interesting. He describes them as creatures able to move through the earth 'without hindrance, as do the Fish in the Waters and the Birds in the Air.' Obviously, and excitingly, he is talking about a pure elemental:

Aside from the rainbow-coloured stockings, this is a conventional enough view of a dwarf. It sums up the ghastly quaintness of the traditional fairy-tale character, perched on a mushroom and beaming vacuously out at the world. Real dwarves were a long way away from the conventional view, however, both in appearance and in character.

One dwarf, Ammez, is noted in the folklore as having a strange and unusual hobby _ for a dwarf. Most of his kind never changed their clothes from one year to the next, and often grew their hair long enough to trip over. Ammez, however, was something of a dandy, with clothes always in the latest (human) style, and a carefully-trimmed beard. His behaviour earned the censure of the dwarves' congress, the Paian, *on more than one occasion.*

probably one of the ancestors of the dwarf-people that humans came to know.

Many of the large earth elementals were killed off or cut down to size in the early, chaotic struggles of the emergent elementals, or in the

Titan Wars. They were enormous in size and power, brutish, aggressive, and almost impossible to communicate with, so anticipating the worst faults of the human superpowers by several million years. It is worth noting that few of them survived: every hand was against them, since nothing else was really safe with them around. But there were many lesser elementals of the kind Paracelsus describes who survived almost unscathed, with very little damaged apart from their sense of security. They were unsettled by the breakup of the earth's crust into drifting tectonic plates: their old channels of traffic and communication were broken, and they could not live in the new lava oozing up through the cracks any more than a man can live in the bare and waterless desert. And so creatures that had once swarmed like ants in the rocky foundations of the planet were divided into small, disorganised communities. For a long time they tried to live as they had, but like fish cut off in separate pools when a river dries out, they became too crowded. It's difficult to understand how overcrowding could have affected creatures less material than a moonbeam, but apparently it did. Then, into these seething, self-destructive melées, came the first human miners.

Humans began to mine very early on. Not for metal – they had not yet learned how to use it – but for flint. One Stone Age mine still survives at Grimes' Graves in Yorkshire, England: a maze of tunnels hollowed out of the rock by antler picks. The earth elementals were vastly impressed by the abilities of these human creatures, and began to try imitating them. They started by building themselves crude bodies out of their own element: granite for bone, clay for flesh, fibrous crystals like asbestos for muscles, and mineral-laden water for blood. After a while they were able to make them work – in some peculiar way – and soon they began to appreciate the advantages of a material form. Concentrated in a body they no longer felt as cramped as they had when they were diffused through several layers of rock. A hundred of them could stand in as many square yards, where before one elemental's scattered energies would have filled twice or three times that space. However, they clearly needed better bodies. The ones they had were, to

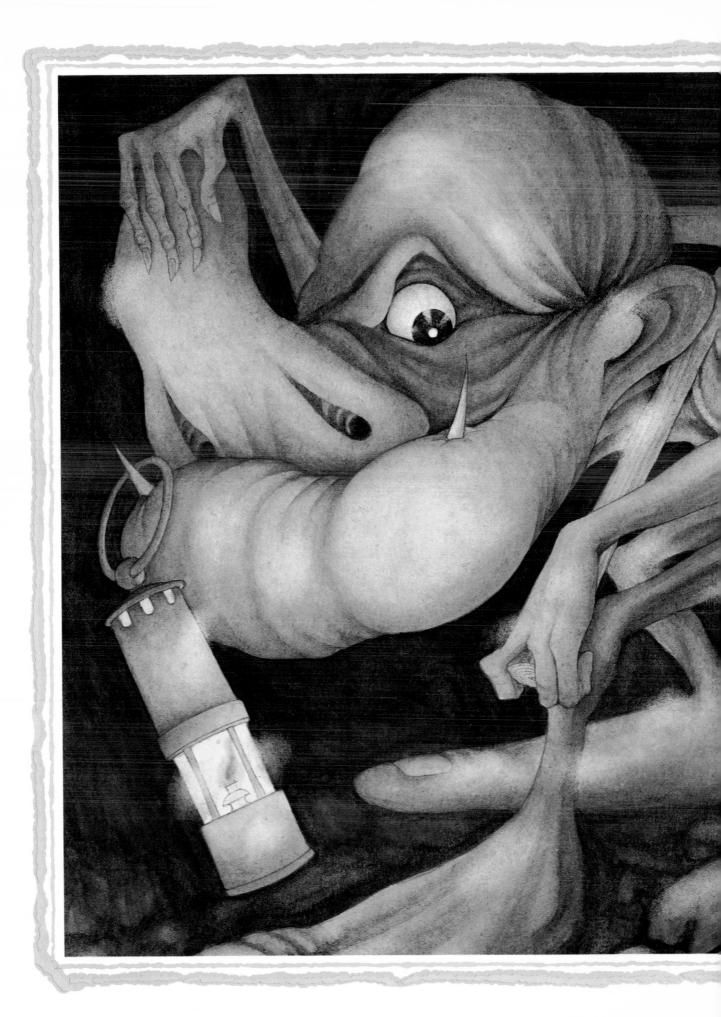

say the least of it, eccentric. Besides, they were fascinated by the craftsmanship of men, and badly wanted to communicate with them. Their crude clay-bodies sent humans shrieking away from what they took to be mortally offended earth-demons. Since the dwarves could not talk shop with a clean pair of heels and a cloud of settling dust, they set to work to build something that looked more reassuring.

Since they were master chemists, with all the mineral resources of the earth even closer than their fingertips, they did not find it at all hard to synthesise a kind of flesh. They took their vital organic chemicals, including complex protein structures, from the great oil pools that were, at the time, just lying there for the taking. However, rather than using anything as feeble as calcium for the skeleton they chose an iron-rich rock similar to haematite, or kidney-ore. Fingernails were made from high-tungsten steel, and hair from a finer variety of steel well suited to picking up the modulated magnetic fields that they still used for talking over long distances. The body was made smaller than human, better

This grotesque, distorted dwarf recalls the earth-elementals' earliest attempts to mould themselves bodies. Since they used the coarse materials of the earth around them, granite and clay and minerals, the result was not good for the mental balance of miners who came on it suddenly. This rather hurt the elementals, who were not actually hostile to men, and they built themselves new bodies that were much more humanoid in appearance, though that was about as much as could be said for them. One or two reactionaries, though, continued to prowl the mines in their old forms, scornful of "oversensitive" humans. Rumous has it, though, that they really relied on the profitable supply of hastily abandoned picks and lanterns their well-timed appearances could yield.

adapted for going through narrow tunnels and workings. A dwarf stood between two and three feet high, and was about the same across the shoulders, presenting an almost perfectly square outline. The appearance was carefully modelled on that of the humans they most admired: the elderly craftsmen. All the same, the resemblance was not *that* close: the hair and beard were like grey wire wool, and the muscles were so enormous that by human standards they looked deformed. As skilled mechanics the dwarves realised that the moment arm of the human limb joint was relatively inefficient, so they lengthened it, creating thick, stubby arms and fingers like fat sausages. The muscles supporting their shoulder-blade assemblies were so thick that they made the dwarves look hunchbacked. They certainly did not have round rosy faces, as Disney and others would like us to believe; their faces were cold, hard, and intense, with waxy white skin usually covered by a layer of mixed grime. Their eyes glittered green or red, because they habitually wore thin lenses of ruby or emerald to protect their eyes from grit or forge sparks.

One way and another, the true descendant of the gnome was as far removed from the sawn-off Dutch Santa Claus in the British suburban front garden as he was from the trolls who occasionally blundered into his tunnellings. Gnomes never had the 'eco-lifestyle' at least one writer has attributed to them, either: they would have been happier in an iron foundry than in a nature preserve, and would have raised no objections to a production line as long as the result was well made. They would most certainly not have minded interfering with the environment. In fact there wasn't much they did care about, aside from making things. They lived on whatever roots and small creatures they came across in the course of their mining, and wore clothes made from skins and coarse vegetable fibre. They could have made more attractive costumes, but they had better things to do with their time. They were restless, feverish creators, spending years at a time over one amazingly intricate and beautiful piece of work, using precious materials almost exclusively. Gems, gold, silver, tin, and amber were transformed by supremely skilled craftsmen with the finest tools ever made into the rarest treasures the earth has ever seen – or hidden. Most of these pieces went into a common hoard for the local group as soon as they were finished or, more commonly, into a private store. Here their maker could gloat over them in secret, showing them only to a trusted few – and with good reason. Dwarves could be obsessively greedy, and many were almost human in their lack of respect for other people's property. It was not unusual for a dwarf to live out his enormously long life without showing anything he had made to another soul, and leave no record of his hoarding-place after his death.

Perhaps this makes the dwarves sound rather unpleasant; in fact, too human. But they did have redeeming features. They had more respect for humans than any of the other elementals, perhaps because they had kept least magic. They preferred manual labour, and so never felt that there was anything beneath their dignity in the human way of life, as many more ancient races obviously did. Their lust for raw materials was insane by human standards – stronger in fact than our desire for food or sex – but when they had enough they were perfectly

happy to share it with humans they had taken a liking to. The dwarves
in the Cornish tin mines came to be known as knockers, because they
would signal the presence of a new seam to their human fellow-miners
by tapping with their hammers. In return the humans would leave them
food, which suited the dwarves very well. They were appalling cooks –
worse even than the trolls – and besides it cut out the irksome breaks to
search for food that interrupted their hunt for fresh ore. In Germany
dwarves even went so far as to borrow a human building now and then
for a celebration, paying with what to their eyes were failed or practise
pieces. Human craftsmen, of course, had never seen work like it.

Their generosity was ill repaid. Tales of dwarfish wealth soon
attracted the attention of that peculiarly human undesirable, the hero, a
superb compound of brains, nerve, selfishness, greed, and brutality.
The largest German dwarf-tribe, the Nibelungs, seem to have secured
the services of the titan-dragon Fafnir to guard their treasure, called the
Rhinegold, though the details are unclear. What is clear is that the hero
Siegfried, after cold-bloodedly murdering Fafnir, proceeded to steal the
Nibelung treasure at sword-point. It did him little good: stolen dwarf-
gold rarely did. There was more than a little dwarf-magic guiding the
spear that finally pierced Siegfried through and through, but its
wielder, the baron Hagen von Tronje, was foolish enough to keep the
Nibelung gold for himself. At the last he threw it into the Rhine to save it
from Attila the Hun, who tortured him to death in an attempt to find out
where it had gone. But the curse, however effective, did the Nibelungs
little good. The rulers and many of the oldest and wisest leaders had
been killed, and they broke up in disorder. Bands of Nibelungs
continued to terrorise remote forest areas and lonely mine workings for

centuries, but their numbers were dwindling, and they never again achieved a fraction of the wealth and security they had once enjoyed.

Treasure-hunters were far from being their biggest headache, especially after Siegfried's fate became common knowledge. The dwarves had an even more pressing problem, and one they should have

Opposite: The master-dwarf Nivek, renowned for his black beard and calculating nature, with his band of followers. He and his tribe frequented the stone quarries of Sussex, England, and there developed extra-long arms to carry larger blocks of stone. In practise, it is said, they found this no help because of the extra strain on their wrists. Like most dwarves, they wore a motley collection of human clothes from many places and times; dwarves lived long and travelled far. Above: They even seem to have found uses for some of the more bizarre human inventions, though where they got them from is anyone's guess. This does not, though, represent some obscure dwarvish perversion; it is simply a dwarf-woman chained securely to the domestic hearth.

recognised from the beginning. There had always been such things as male and female elementals, so like the other races the dwarves had no trouble carrying over the distinction into their new bodies. But for obvious reasons the distinction had been more mental than physical, and it had never had much connection with the reproductive process. A 'male' and a 'female' could separate aspects of themselves and combine them to make a third individual, but as often as not this was very casually done. It broke the ice at social gatherings, and if the newcomer did not seem particularly amusing he could easily be reabsorbed. But in their new way of life the dwarves made the mistake of trying to imitate human beings too closely. They were constantly thundering that a woman's place was in the home, slaving over a hot – well, not a hot stove, since dwarves never bothered to cook their food, but a hot *forge*: that was the job for a woman! Unfortunately the dwarf women did not share the obsessive drive to create that was the dwarfish equivalent of *machismo*, though that never worried their menfolk in the slightest. In fact, there is no record of anyone ever *seeing* a dwarf-woman: they were kept in strict purdah by their husbands, though not for reasons of chastity. *Someone* had to keep working those bellows, after all.

It took the dwarf-women a surprisingly long time to decide that they had nothing to lose but their chains (literally, in most cases), but in the end they did. The revolt was led by a tough-minded dwarfish

From Wagner's opera Siegfried, *the devious, calculating and thoroughly unsavory, dwarf-smith Mime hammers away at swordmaking. He has reared the human hero Siegfried, not out of kindness but as a kind of secret weapon to use against the dragon Fafnir, guardian of the Rhinegold hoard; that done, he plans to dispose of Siegfried and take the treasure for himself. To kill Fafnir, the human will need a sword, and Mime simply cannot make one that will stand up to the boy's strength. One after another, they are snapped on the anvil they were forged on – but when Siegfried tests a sword he makes for himself, the anvil shatters.*

89

Lysistrata who put their demands firmly on the line. No more pumping their husbands' bellows, no more hammering away at their gold leaf, no more of those wretched prickly diamonds lying around cluttering up the tunnel. The effect on the male dwarves was traumatic. In humans it might have led to diminished virility, male menopause, and all the other symptoms of panic. In dwarves it led to a lack of confidence in their abilities, which was even more serious. After all, what else could they *do*? Tradition has it that in this blackly depressing time the game of football was invented, as a kind of self-destructive ritual of applied meaninglessness. Finally the male dwarves were driven to violence. Females were grabbed and chained back to their bellows, assisted by fearsome threats of beating and starvation if they failed to put their backs into the pumping. For the females, their consciousness now raised to its limits, this was the last straw. Many of them had been dubious about bodies and similar human affectations from the very

The famous story of the Elves and the Shoemaker was not entirely elvish nonsense, merely a little mixed up. The people involved were certainly not Elves, who tended to be either weak and malign or else remote from human affairs altogether. In any case they were never much use with their hands. It seems to have been a group of unusually amiable dwarves who helped the old shoemaker. There is no record of their having charged him double time for overtime and unsociable hours, which is unheard of with dwarves; the words for altruism and insanity are almost, if not entirely, the same in most dwarf languages. Perhaps they were just glad of the chance to practise their mass-production skills, and passed on the cost to another customer.

beginning, and now things were worse than they could ever have feared. More than one took the obvious step of letting her body fall apart where it stood and resuming her elemental freedom with a parting Bronx cheer to her domineering mate. A few, with malice aforethought, took the opportunity to explode, and mess up their husbands' precious workshops. In their long years of servitude the women had never become as tied to their material form as their menfolk, so they had little difficulty in giving it up. Not so the males. The few who tried to follow their absconding mates were not heard from again. The rest just sighed philosophically, picked the innumerable fragments of iron bone and steel nails out of the wall, the tool-chest, the bellows, the water-pump, and anything else that had been around when their wives made their sudden departures, and settled down to try and copy the newfangled watermills the humans were making, or to figure out a way to get wind-power three hundred yards underground.

But their hearts weren't really in it. Their numbers dwindled, and the Transcript makes it clear that many of them were soon caught up in the Retreat. They lingered in a few places like the Cornish tin mines until as late as the eighteenth century, but after that there is little or no mention of them. And given the way man is eating into the resources they used to share with us, it is hardly surprising. If there *are* any dwarves left around they must be incurable optimists.

And the women? Nobody knows. Not all of them went, of course, though most did. Perhaps it was one of them that Paracelsus or his informant ran into, paddling delicately along some long-fossilised seabed, bathing happily in the ancient solar energy trapped in the rocks. And why not? After a few thousand years of bellows-pumping hadn't they earned a holiday?

SHAPE-SHIFTERS

One of the most alarming results of elemental-human blending was the appearance of the shape-shifters. On the elemental side they were descended from exceptionally able and adaptable creatures such as the titan Proteus, who could take on a bewildering variety of shapes in quick succession. His ability to transform himself into a rope of running water, a roaring fire, a sea-serpent, a lascivious mermaid, a ravening lion, and a handful of sand – all in the space of a few seconds – proved the undoing of many would-be heroes (whose names, of course, have not survived) and the making of those with enough strength, courage, and sheer idiocy to hang onto him till he ran out of ideas. Then he would

Shape-shifters – perhaps the most terrifying legacy left to us by the elemental invasion of our dimension. The shape-shifting gene, passed down from ancestral gods to their human and semi-human descendants, unleashed the darkest passions and the most destructive violence of which our kind is capable. With few exceptions, those gifted with the power of changing their form assumed the shape of their own most savage and brutal impulses.

Shapeshifters tended to make themselves not so much into animals as into their idea of what the animals looked like. This usually meant they became caricatures of the original creatures, as here.

tell any number of valuable secrets. Luckily for lesser beings, it was rare for elementals to retain so much control over the bodies they assumed. Many gods and titans could change shape, but they rarely did so. Perhaps it hurt. The Norse god Loki was an exception. We have already seen how he turned himself into a mare to lure the magical stallion Svadilfari away from the building of Asgard. In fact he seems to have thrown himself a little too far into the role: some time later he gave birth

to a foal. This probably amused his fellow gods, who had little love for him anyway, but the foal did grow up to become the mighty Sleipnir, steed of Odin himself. Loki took on other shapes as well, including a giantess, a falcon, and a salmon, usually in the course of organising one of his con-tricks or escaping from its results. Once he tried to prevent the forging of Thor's great hammer, Mjollnir, by turning himself into an enormous gadfly and stinging the dwarf-smiths, but all that happened

was that the handle came out a little short.

The god Zeus was also more than usually adept, but he reserved his shape-changing for important business. By all accounts his most important business was seduction: he seemed to think they lacked style

Left: Loki, arch shape-shifter of the gods. After engineering the death of the bright god, Baldr, Loki was hunted by other gods. He hid himself near the Frananger Falls, taking the shape of a salmon; but the gods dragged the river with a net, and in a last desperate effort to get free Loki leapt out of the water and began to transform himself into a falcon, his other favourite disguise. Before he could escape, Thor grabbed him; and now Loki lies imprisoned beneath the earth until the end of the world. Above: A selkie, one of a beautiful race of shape-shifting water elementals who normally took the shape of seals but could also adopt this strange, almost human appearance.

99

unless they were carried out in the shape of a swan, a bull, a shower of gold – or whatever . . . Just the same, his transformation into an eagle in order to carry off the boy Ganymede doesn't seem to have fooled anyone. It may have been one of his more orthodox affairs that passed the shape-shifting genes on to the human race in the first place – with some very unhappy results. Elementals seem to have taken a callous amusement in passing on weird abilities to their human children without thought for the long-term consequences.

The children of Proteus and Zeus certainly seem to have been with us since very early days. Cave paintings in the Dordogne region of France, at Altamira in Spain, and in many other places, show mysterious and beautiful images of men with animal heads and shoulders. Understandably, archaeologists have interpreted these as shamans dancing in animal skins or masks, like those the Haida and Kwakiutl Indians still wear at their ceremonies. But the Transcript sheds a sinister new light on them. Maybe those figures were not masked – or if they were, was it an animal they represented? There is an eerie, lifelike quality about those heads that doesn't suggest either masks or hunting trophies. One carved piece of bone found at Isturitz shows a picture of two bison on one side, one with arrows in its hindquarters. On the other side a man is shown chasing a woman, both on all fours. A peculiar love charm, as archaeologists suggest? Perhaps. But the man

Most shapeshifters were too unstable in mind to control their abilities. Legend suggests, though, that there were a few who could transform themselves into almost any creature – or even combination of creatures, as here – that they chose. Fortunately for the rest of us, though, they were always rare. It was worse when vampiric air elementals chanced to animate a body with latent shapeshifting ability (overleaf). To their other powers they added that of flitting silently and secretly across the night sky.

100

has a strange blunt face – and there is an arrow in the woman's thigh. This must be a sinister love, if it is love at all.

'Sinister' is the only word that is really appropriate in a discussion of shape-shifting. It sounds like a marvellous magical ability, the sort of talent we poor underprivileged humans should be grateful for. Imagine the freedom and liberation of becoming, at will, a horse, a bounding gazelle, or a cheetah. Imagine confronting a would-be mugger and calling up the shape of a bear, a lion, or a wolf. Not to mention the subtler advantages of becoming, quite literally, a fly on the wall. It ought to be like that, and perhaps to begin with it was. But things quickly changed for the worse.

To begin with, most humans chose power rather than grace. Their

animal forms were almost always malignant, even when the real animals they copied were not normally vicious. Wolves, especially lone wolves, are less savage – and less courageous – than a domestic dog. Unless they are starving, and in a pack, they do not hunt man. They avoid him. Yet werewolves, and their African cousins the *Agiotos*, or leopardmen, always appear as ravening and irresistible killers. Against these unnatural monsters even the bravest hunter bars his door and trembles. Why?

The problem is that in nine cases out of ten shape-shifting seems to be tied up with serious mental disturbance. In other words, shape-shifters are almost always schizophrenics, changing personality at the same time as they change body shape. The trouble starts because it is always the second, aberrant personality that chooses the shape they assume. Robert Louis Stevenson portrayed this with chilling accuracy in *Dr Jekyll and Mr Hyde*, which he based on a recurrent nightmare he had suffered. His description of Mr Hyde reads like that of a shape-shifter frozen in the moment of his transformation, as if by the last weak remains of an inherited ability boosted, perhaps, by the infamous potion. What would he have become if the transformation had been completed? Such a character will inevitably clothe itself in the most fearsome shape it can imagine, moulding it to its distorted self-image. That is what makes were-creatures so fearsome: each is a human psychopath, given animal senses, strength and weaponry. Even its elemental ancestors would blanch.

But a few shape-shifters were more or less harmless, and some were

even attractive. Many Norse and Russian legends speak of beautiful women who can take the form of swans. It is another self-image, of course, but quite appropriate for a lovely girl. Yet there is a hint of aberration even in these delightful creatures. They seem to have rather vague, flighty personalities; rather as though they were beginning a schizoid flight from reality. Several swan-maidens, notably the one who married Volund, the Norse master-smith, simply flew away one day without warning and without reason. And heroes who got themselves entangled with swan-maids seemed to come to sticky ends, as in the legend that inspired Tchaikovsky's *Swan Lake*.

By and large, it is just as well that the shape-shifting ability seems to be dying out among human beings. We cannot be sure why. Perhaps many of the most adept – and so most unbalanced – shape-shifters

Left: The shape-shifting gene, the true 'beast beneath the skin', lingers on in all of us, concealing itself beneath a mask of respectability and civility.
Above: One of the stranger products of elemental miscegenation: a cross between a lynx, a gryphon, and a serpent perches on a rock pinnacle.

simply preferred to remain in their animal forms. Eventually they must have lost all human memories, living and dying as the beasts they mimicked. And perhaps their own insanity meant that few of them had children to carry their dark abilities onwards into the future. Besides, tradition suggests that a shape-shifter's family were liable to be among his first victims.

But one or two remnants of the old power linger on. Perhaps that recurring dream of Stevenson's was the last stirring of his own Mr Hyde. Look around you at people in the street, or even at some of the world's leading statesmen and women. Is something in their makeup striving to model their bodies into their own self-image? It isn't hard to find politicians and public figures who look like bears or pigs or foxes, psychotic African dictators who look exactly like gorillas or, closer to home, pretty girls who remind you irresistibly of vixens, cats, swans – or chattering canaries.

Are they all halfway to being – something else?

SEMI-HUMANS

Semi-humans of many types appeared on the earth soon after the arrival of the magical races. Aside from the trolls, most of the ex-elementals seemed to find human men and women very attractive. The result was a clutch of gods and demigods, among them such famous legendary heroes as Hercules and Achilles. The ravishingly beautiful Helen of Sparta, 'the face that launched a thousand ships', was the daughter of the god Zeus by Leda, who was probably a mortal woman. In this particular encounter Zeus appeared in the form of a swan: but he remembered to keep his genes mostly human. Some of the Norse gods who disregarded this precaution produced swan-maidens.

Beauty and the Beast: Edmund Dulac's interpretation of a story first recorded in ancient Greece. Many of the commoner semi-human forms – centaurs, satyrs, sphinxes, and the like – developed small, self-contained communities, but inevitably the mixture of elemental and human stock produced sports and mutations accepted by no-one. The image of the Beast, powerful, magical, yet starved of the love it really needs, remains with us to this day.

But it was the were-creatures who caused the greatest confusion. Besides ensuring that their disreputable genes were carried in human bloodlines all the way down to the present day, they also tended to produce offspring that were, to put it kindly, neither one thing nor the other. Notorious examples include the unfortunate minotaur (the offspring of a were-bull and Pasiphae, queen of Crete, which had the body of a man and the head of a bull) and the whole tribe of centaurs. The gods, as usual, claimed to have had a hand in this: their story was that the demigod Ixion, lusting after Hera, the consort of Zeus, was tricked into lying with a cloud in the form of the goddess, and from this strange union the first centaur was born. Whatever the private vices of Ixion, this is clearly a very tall story. The Bremen Transcript suggests that the centaur tribe was fathered by a herd of enthusiastic were-stallions after a drinking bout on the slopes of Mount Pelion. Whatever their origin, the centaurs were one of the few semi-human groups to breed consistently true. Once again the Transcript account seems to be taken from a verbatim narrative by the titan Corineus, who gives a clear impression of their everyday life. Centaurs, he explains need six meals a day, three for each stomach, and as a result they frequently suffer from indigestion, not to mention problems with cud-chewing. Female centaurs, despite spirited attempts to win themselves equal rights, are generally discouraged by their mates from wandering about the countryside. This is because centaurs in general find clothes inconvenient; and the sight of a female centaur galloping across open country is not easily forgotten.

Centaur males are often passionately attracted to human women. The famous battle with the Lapiths during the marriage feast of Peirithous began in precisely this way, and once again the main culprit was strong drink. Human women are rarely willing to return the centaurs' ardour: their mixed diet makes for appalling breath, and however attractive the human end may be, the stallion hindquarters pose an altogether insuperable problem. In any case, their physique is probably a little too powerful for amours with humans. Few centaurs survive into late maturity, but those that do share one characteristic at least with sphinxes, the offspring of mortal unions with were-lions: a deep wisdom. The combination of magical and human genes always seems to produce something exceptionally evil, exceptionally powerful, or exceptionally wise. Sphinxes, however, have an unpleasant habit of speaking in riddles, combined with a short temper inherited from their

Opposite: A shape-shifting werewolf, ancestor of many semi-human types. Overleaf: The medieval bestiaries recorded scores of magical and semi-human creatures long since lost to human knowledge in the Great Retreat. It is possible that many of them were deliberately created by gods and titans in the course of the Titan Wars, but many more were the children of accident and chance. From left to right they are (front) a gryphon; a mantichore, a ferocious human-headed carnivore with three interlocking rows of teeth; a basilisk, whose breath or glance could kill, said to be hatched by a serpent from a cock's egg; and (back) a unicorn, a beautiful physical embodiment of magic; and an Assyrian human-headed winged bull, possessed of enormous elemental power.

lion halves. As a result those unable to guess their riddles tend to have a high mortality rate. On the other hand, human beings who *do* understand what sphinxes are talking about are usually irritating and rather showy types destined to come to a bad end. Oedipus, of course, was a case in point. When he guessed the Theban sphinx's riddle 'What has four legs in the morning, two at midday, and three in the evening'* and then tried to cap it with one of his own, the outraged semi-human told him to go home to mother. Oedipus promptly pushed her off her rock, later reporting it as suicide.

Sphinxes are generally solitary creatures, but when they do appear in groups the dominance of the female seems to reflect their lion ancestry. Male sphinxes do exist, and very impressive beings they are, but they are firmly controlled by their partners. If a female sphinx suspects her mate of misbehaving, she will often subject him to a stream of well-worn proverbs, wise saws, and instances. They are probably the originators of this time-worn technique, which females of all races have used to bring even the most refractory males into line. Probably it was no more – and no less – than this that constituted the fabled 'wisdom of the sphinx'. Sphinxes prefer desert conditions, and their tawny colour allows them to conceal themselves in the sand if danger threatens.

Corineus had obviously enjoyed close and friendly contact both with centaurs and with sphinxes during the golden age before the Titan Wars, although the Transcript account suggests that by the time of Numenos both these ancient races were all but extinct. However, there was one semi-human race that had survived unchanged: the delightful fauns, or satyrs, who lived in the woods and forests of Greece and seem to have travelled as far north as the Black Forest. These footloose creatures, half-human and half-goat, were extremely agile, and since they were among the first of the magical races to appreciate human music we may even owe the art of the dance to them. The leader of the satyrs, Pan, invented the first woodwind instrument – the pan-pipes – on which all later instruments were modelled. The gods always claimed that Pan was a demigod, but then the gods were always anxious to take the credit for anything pleasant or useful that came into the world. There is no reason to believe that Pan was anything other than an unusually large, powerful, and intelligent satyr.

Another human invention that the satyrs, like the centaurs, enjoyed – usually too much and too often – was strong liquor. Few of them had much of a head for drink, since unlike humans they never developed any kind of a resistance to alcohol. The effects were similar to those seen among Indian tribes in the American West, and may account for the appearance of satyrs in later stories as wild, uncouth, and unpleasant roisterers always ready to waylay and ravish innocent human maidens. There is no doubt that, like many of the magical peoples, they once liked the company of human beings. However, unlike centaurs, they also seem to have been attractive to humans. Their faces were normally brown, slightly wrinkled, and pleasant, capped with curly hair that almost concealed their pointed ears and goats' horns, while their shaggy goats' legs, with their rich coat of black fur,

*The answer, of course, is 'a man'.

were warm, strokable, and generally very clean. Unfortunately, their life of merriment and debauchery aged them rather quickly. Most satyrs

Above: A satyr, half-man and half-goat, is woken from his more than usually drunken slumber. Satyrs, though fond of the Arcadian equivalent of a night on the tiles, had no head whatsoever for drink. It is easy to see how this lithe and graceful creature must have enjoyed the arts of music and the dance, especially if he could find a pretty nymph for a dancing- partner. Much of the bad reputation of satyrs is probably due to the activities of the 16th and 17th century witches, whose familiars copied the form of these innocent semi-humans in their attempts to awe gullible and superstitious human dupes.

Left: Folklore preserves many memories of magic: not only semi-humans such as the swan- maids (left), but also witches flying on broomsticks at Halloween (right), the Green people (top left), the high elves (top right), and the old gods (foreground). Above: An Agioto, or African leopard-man, caught in semi-human form as he changes from man to beast.

were past their best by about the age of 25, and the figure of Silenus, so well known in the Roman world, shows what happened after that. Silenus is invariably shown as fat, clumsy, and intoxicated: a sad comment on the corrupting influence of human beings on this charming people.

Other semi-humans were less desirable. The Gorgons, and in particular Medusa, whose hair was a tangled nest of poisonous snakes, were so repulsive that their glance was reputed to turn men to stone. When Medusa was finally killed by the human hero Perseus, it appears that a sphinx he met on his way back across Egypt was over-inquisitive about what he was carrying in his bag, and thus became the first stone sphinx in Egypt and the model for many later carvings. The harpies, half-woman and half-bird, had all the desirability of a flock of oversized pigeons with bad digestion. In general we can be grateful that few, if any, of these races have survived to the present day.

VAMPIRES, GHOSTS, AND GHOULS

Not surprisingly, the elementals who were least successful in their attempts to win a physical form were the air spirits. Although their magical abilities were well developed, their ability to affect the physical world had always been slight. They even found it difficult to take over the body of a living creature: their power was simply not great enough to sway a living mind for any length of time. So only one course, and that an extremely unpleasant one, was left open to them if they wished to keep abreast of their fellow-elementals: corpse-stealing. It is a measure of their desperation that many of them were willing to try it. Suicides were particularly popular candidates because their time of death could

Ghosts, the visible forms of elementals who failed in their efforts to steal dying human bodies. The ancient and fish-like smell of these hapless air spirits, noted by more than one ghost-hunter, is an emotional reaction to their plight. Once they were free to roam every dimension, until their own greed left them trapped at a single spot on a single world, doomed to relive their failure over and over again until the end of time.

be predicted with some accuracy. Under the right conditions, as the last breath of a dying mortal passed into the air, a crowd of elementals would be struggling to take possession of the body. Sometimes – but only very rarely – one would succeed, lying quiet until the body was entombed and then reanimating it, usually in the form of a vampire. More often, their success was only partial, and they took the form of the dead mortal without gaining the substance. Such spirits are not able to leave the place where they attempted their unsuccessful transfer, and this almost certainly accounts for the many accredited sightings of ghosts throughout the world. Nor is it hard to understand why so many of these spirits appear to be suffering or in despair. Imagine the feelings of an air spirit shackled to one spot in an unfamiliar and hostile dimension and yet denied the use of a physical body.

Opposite: Most vampires did not survive more than a few years in their stolen flesh before they were discovered and destroyed. But a very small number lived an entire human lifetime, or even several lifetimes, without anyone so much as suspecting their existence. Moving in a world of twilight, darkness, and secrecy, alongside humanity without being a part of it, these creatures learned a great and terrible wisdom. Some, driven by a burning envy of the life they could never really share, became implacable enemies of humanity, working by every means in their power to spread death, suffering, and fear. Others, like this one, became figures of almost tragic nobility. But even these could not do without the blood that kept their bodies whole and unblemished; and no vampire ever seems to have found it possible to abandon, of its own free will, the physical existence it had struggled so hard to achieve.

Those who succeeded in becoming vampires did not seem to fare much better. Blood, apparently the staple food of the vampire, was simply used to keep the dead flesh in some semblance of its living state. That and magic were usually all that held it together, and as soon as the elemental was forced to abandon its hold, the body crumbled into dust. By the very nature of their lives, vampires were forced to operate at night, and then spent the day recovering their energies. During this period, of course, they were very vulnerable. When active, the vampire would often seem to have memories of its earthly life, but this was simply because the elemental controlling it had access to all its host's memories, and would often use them to gain entrance to a house where it could feed. This is why many vampires appeared to haunt their own family circle. Aside from its native magical abilities, the vampire showed little sign of its elemental origins other than an exceptionally keen sense of smell. This may account for its well-known aversion to garlic and other aromatic herbs.

Left: The legend of the vampire, which could supposedly transform itself into a bat or a cloud of mist at will, may be built on the long-hidden truth about these creatures revealed by the Bremen Transcript: that they were in reality air elementals clothed in stolen flesh. The image of these sinister beings in flight across a cloud-wracked moonlit sky is so powerful that it has almost replaced the older, grimmer tales in the popular imagination. The truth is that a vampire in its stolen body was entombed in flesh that could only be kept whole by magic. Occasionally a powerful vampire like the Icelandic Thorolf Clubfoot might gain enough strength to take over the body of a living creature, but this was exceptional. Most vampires lived their miserable lives among the tombs they had robbed in the lust for physical form.

127

Stories of the walking dead are reported from all over the world, though the worst visitations of vampires seem to have been in central Europe during the early middle ages. In fact the Greek equivalent of our phrase 'bringing coals to Newcastle' is 'taking vampires to Santorini', which even comparatively recently was a notorious haunt of these *vrykolakes*, as they are called. It is now well-known that Santorini (also called Thera) was the site of one of the world's most destructive volcanic eruptions during the Minoan period (about 2000-1500 BC). It has even been suggested that the explosion of Thera in about 1500 BC may have been the origin of the legend of Atlantis and the beginning of the end of the Minoan civilisation. There is one further possibility: that Thera was the site of a titanic struggle between air and fire elementals. Air elementals, finding fruitful ground for the breeding of vampires in the superstitions of the local people, were gathering in force on Thera. The sudden increase in numbers of these usually solitary creatures alarmed the other magical races, and as a last resort the decision was taken to destroy the vampires' physical hosts and their new breeding ground in one fell swoop. The only way this object could be achieved was to stage a catastrophe on a colossal scale; but in an age that still favoured the old gods there must be no sign of their active intervention. And so the fire elementals were sent to stir the hidden embers of an ancient volcano: and one of mankind's most ancient and enduring legends was born as the island of Thera was literally blown apart. Vampires still haunt the shattered crescent of Santorini, but they will never again pose the threat that they did in Minoan times.

Norse myth and legend makes it clear that vampires were not the semi-substantial creatures of later story, but horrifyingly real and solid beings. The most famous example, Glam, was an Icelandic shepherd who was literally frightened to death by a particularly virulent air elemental who afterwards stole his corpse. In the saga account Glam's bloated body returns to haunt the house where he used to live. He frightens the house-folk, bounces on the main roof-beams, kills the

Opposite: Despite his terrifying reputation the Vampire represents one of the elementals' least succcessful attempts to take on physical form. Restricted by its need for secrecy and the feeble magic that bound it to its stolen body, it was almost a pitiable creature. Overleaf: But when it inhabited a shapeshifter's body and became a werewolf or acquired the strength to become a ghoul, then the stake provided the only human weapon against a terrible adversary.

animals, and generally makes a complete pest of himself until he attracts the attention of the hero Grettir the Strong. Grettir eventually engages him in hand-to-hand combat, and since he is without fear he has little difficulty in overpowering the vampire and cutting off its head. In a final and powerful moment of spite, the elemental animates the severed head long enough to terrify Grettir and leave him with a vision of two enormous eyes that haunts him whenever he is in danger. From that moment on, Grettir's eventual defeat and death are only a matter of time.

In the case of Thorolf Clubfoot, another Icelandic vampire, the controlling elemental was even more stubborn. When the body had been burned after a succession of hauntings, the displaced air spirit managed to enter the body of a pregnant cow and win control of the embryo. It had its revenge when it was born as a bull-calf a few months later and was ultimately able to gore to death the man who had burned its first stolen body.

Ghouls seem to be another case of possession by an air elemental, since they were often associated with vampires. The power of ghouls was similar to that of the Icelandic vampires, and they required more solid food than their blood-sucking cousins: but like many air elementals they were rather cowardly, and preferred to feed on corpses and carrion rather than hunting for living prey. Like hyenas, they tended to move in packs, and could be driven away from their grisly feast by anyone with the courage to oppose them.

THE WATER FOLK

The water elementals were something of a race apart, taking little interest in the squabbles and struggles of their fellows. They were even less interested in humanity, at least to begin with. After all, what could humans *do* in their element – except drown? This may explain why water elementals were so slow to take on material bodies, or any kind of solid form, for that matter. Legends the world over speak of sea-gods appearing as towering waves, columns of foam, and enormous tides, but these things were child's play to a powerful elemental, and when they did join the brawling of the other elementals they showed a certain lack of finesse. The floods they raised during the second Titan War were

Finnish mythology records how a water elemental, Luonnatar, helped in the creation of the world. Weary of her sterile existence, she threw herself into the sea, and for centuries she floated there until an eagle appeared in the sky. It built its nest on her knee, and laid its eggs there. The water spirit cast them away from her, and they shattered: but from their ruins the earth, the heavens, the sun, the moon, and the stars were made.

far too large and proved incredibly difficult to get rid of. Hardly surprising that many myths speak of heroic gods who managed to rescue one or another patch of land from overflowing rivers and oceans. Among these early land reclamation experts were the Hawaiian Tangoloa, the South American Bochicha, the Indian Rama, and many more. Probably they were diplomats rather than warriors. Water elementals were difficult to threaten, unless you could band together enough of the elusive fire elementals to vaporize them.

Yet despite their enormous power and freedom the water elementals did eventually begin to experiment with material bodies. Since they lacked the experience of the more sophisticated gods and giants, these early attempts made up in size what they lacked in refinement. Huge masses of animal plankton, floating kelp, algae, weeds, and half-decayed organic debris from the seabed would be scooped together to form a crude and unstable body of fantastic size. A few of these mobile mudbanks were still around in medieval times; these were the monstrous 'island beasts', or Iasconia, encountered by such travellers as Sindbad, St Brendan, and Sir John Mandeville. As a rule the luckless explorer did not discover the true nature of his uncharted island until he landed on it. The beast was too insensitive to notice the landing itself, but sooner or later its visitors would get round to lighting a fire. By the time this message got through to the controlling elemental, the ill-constructed monster was usually already falling apart, but would in any case submerge, leaving its startled passengers quite literally at sea. It seems likely that a few of the younger or less intelligent elementals even took this up as a rather cheap form of practical joke.

Fire, not surprisingly, proved an ideal weapon against the more aggressive of these island beasts, and was particularly successful in the case of the last really large and dangerous Iasconia on record: the so-called Meister Stoor Worm. Early in the Dark Ages this dim-witted navigational hazard was ravaging the shipping lanes in the Orkney area. A young seaman named Asepatlr mounted a harpoon on the bows of his fishing boat, tipped it with peats soaked in blazing pitch, and rowed straight into the monster's throat. It was later said that the resulting corpse became a real island: Iceland, no less. This must be a slight exaggeration. No Iasconia grew that big. Not *quite*.

The best estimate of their size is given by Erik Ludvigsen Pontopiddan, bishop of Bergen, Norway, in his *Natural History of Norway* (1752-53; translated 1755):

> 'Our fishermen . . . when they row several miles out to Sea . . . and by their Situation . . . expect to find 80 or 100 fathoms depth, it often happens that they do not find above 20 or 30, and sometimes less . . . by this they judge the Kraken is at the bottom. They say this creature creates these unusual shallows . . . Its back or upper part . . . seems to be in appearance about an English mile and a half in circumference (some say more, but I choose the least for greater certainty) . . . looks at first like a number of small islands, surrounded with something that floats and fluctuates like weeds . . . '

But only the dimmest, least enterprising elementals were content to remain in lumpish, semi-vegetable bodies like this. The more ambitious among them chose to imitate the shape of the gods, and before long sea-elementals in more or less humanoid shape had joined the ranks of every race of would-be deities. Yet they still remained independent and aloof characters. Njord (the Celtic Nerthus), the Japanese Ouata-Tsumi, the Finnish Ahti, and especially Poseidon-Neptunus, were among the most powerful members of their respective pantheons, but as newcomers they tended to stand on their dignity, and their short tempers were matched by uncomfortably long memories. As the Greek adventurer Odysseus found, it was never wise to offend the sea-gods, even if other gods were supposed to be looking after you. Zeus himself could only shield Odysseus from the most violent extremes of Poseidon's wrath, and it took the combined power of all the Babylonian gods to subdue the ravening sea-goddess Tiamat.

As if to underline their independence, many sea-gods were on better terms with the titans than the other gods would have liked. Njord married the giantess Skadi, though it was not one of the world's most successful unions: she complained that the noise of the seagulls kept her awake, and became an early champion of the women's movement when she insisted that at least half their time should be spent in her comfortable inland castle in the mountains. Njord unfortunately found the art of skiing beyond him, and was in any case too far from his native element for comfort. The marriage, alas, foundered. Poseidon eventually fought the titans at the side of Zeus, but he had inherited his realm from the aging titan Oceanus, whose daughter Amphitrite he married. He had affairs with other titans, too, resulting in some rather weird offspring. Among them, by all accounts, was the race of the *cyclopes*, and he certainly seems to have been fond of these unlovely children. They often acted as his agents in the course of his favourite sport – fouling up the plans of his fellow-deity, Zeus. It amused the sea-god to prove himself as powerful as the chief of the gods, but it never dawned on him that Zeus had something called brains. As with many of the more powerful sea-elementals, they were not his own strong point.

Many of the less powerful sea-elementals were in fact much brighter. Lacking great magic they needed intelligence to stay alive, and tended to band together for protection, which made them even more like human beings. They were able to study early man at close quarters: at some point our ancestors seem to have spent a lot of time in the water – the patterns of our body hair still resemble those of aquatic mammals – and many elementals got to know us there. On the whole they seem to have liked us, because they took on very human form. Inland elementals, living in lakes, rivers, and springs, would often take the form of beautiful women – the water-nymphs of Greek legend, beloved of the Arcadian shepherds. But they were not always so friendly. The Rusalka of Slavonic myth was no less beautiful, but the young men she lured into the water rarely came out again. Whether that was the

The sea-people were often to be found in the waters around large island chains like the British Isles or Japan. Some Japanese folk-tales may be dim memories of the sea-peoples' role in the wars between gods and titans (overleaf).

Rusalka's doing or the result of sheer exhaustion, of course, we will never know . . .

For some reason the inland water elementals of the British Isles were even less friendly. Perhaps it was because they had more difficulty in creating a really attractive physical body. With a few exceptions they were as hideous as they were dangerous. Jenny Greenteeth and Peg Powler, two homicidal female river spirits from the north of England, appeared in the form of slimy, skeletally thin creatures; and with these rather limited powers of attraction they probably *stayed* thin. The *glaistig*, another Scots river creature, had more market sense. Like the Rusalki, she used beauty as bait for her human prey. The *each-uisge* (Gaelic for 'water horse') or kelpie of Scotland could take on a human form, usually that of a good-looking young man, but most often appeared to its victims as a splendid stallion. Anyone mounting this docile-looking animal would at once be borne off into the depths of the loch. But the champion monster of all was the spectacularly revolting *nuckelavee* of northern Scotland, a nasty blend of human and horse that was almost certainly a psychotic kelpie, unable to settle into either of its two forms. To add the final touch of loathsomeness, its skin was transparent, revealing black blood coursing through yellow veins.

The nuckelavee was a creature of the shoreline, not really at home in either salt or fresh water. A very different elemental race lived in the open sea, forming a greater and far more formidable people than their inland relatives. Their elemental ancestors had also admired the human form, but found it poorly adapted for swimming in the open sea. They began a series of rather radical experiments combining human bodies with those of other, more sea-oriented forms. Some of the results had to be seen to be disbelieved, and probably formed the basis of many a good tavern yarn in the early days of seafaring, but eventually a viable form emerged in the merfolk.

The merfolk females (mermaids) and males (tritons) both combined a streamlined and muscular fishlike tail with a human upper half containing the chief human assets: brains and hands. Fully grown, their bodies were larger than the human average: a mermaid with legs would have stood at least six and a half feet tall, and a triton nearer nine. In fact the tritons were so bulky and dark-skinned that they were often mistaken for huge seals or dolphins; the human resemblance was less obvious than that of the mermaids. Mermaids, with their light skin, long, fair hair, and rather obvious female attributes, proved hard for women-starved sailors to ignore. Early seafarers, in fact, made a perfect pest of themselves trying to catch these beautiful creatures. Alas, more than their tails were modelled along the lines of fish, a characteristic that laid those unlucky enough to be caught open to brutal mistreatment from their disappointed captors. Small wonder that the merfolk began

Mermaids, after unfortunate experiences with humans, tended to fight back. It is no accident that they are often depicted, as here, with bodies of drowned sailors tangled in the weed below them; the ancient Greeks, who were often on good terms with elementals, had legends of the Sirens, who lured men to their doom with beauty and song. The mermaid here, as in the old ballad, has a glass in her hand; it reflects a storm-tossed ship.

The image of the mermaid, remote and beautiful, recurs throughout human literature. Shakespeare, in A Midsummer Night's Dream, depicts the mermaid's song as so beautiful that stars come down to hear it. Hans Christian Andersen, in The Little Mermaid, (opposite) dramatised the tragic consequences of a mermaid's love for a human.

to fight back, developing an early lead in the art of submarine warfare. Seafearers began to dread the mere sight of a mermaid. If she noticed them, the chances were that their ship was already doomed. In the words of the old ballad:

'T'was on Friday morn when we set sail
And our ship not far from land
When the captain he espied a lovely mermaid
With a comb and glass in her hand . . .
And up spake the captain of our gallant ship
And a fearful man was he
"I have wedded a wife in fair Bristol town
And tonight she a widow will be . . . '

It's hard to blame the merfolk. After all, if their haunts had become well known, sensation seekers would have arrived in droves with nets, harpoons, hooks, and all the other subtle instruments of human curiosity. Today it would be scalpels, pins, slabs, and slides; but it all comes to the same thing.

In the cold northern waters the fish-form was not so well-adapted, and female elementals had reluctantly to forgo the pleasure of staring at their beautiful torsos and faces in mirrors stolen from wrecks or thrown out as bait by infatuated sailors. Merfolk in these regions had to model their hindquarters on those of the seal, and though the upper half remained human in appearance, it was usually rather more hairy. These seal-folk were found across an enormous area from the north of Scotland to the Arctic waters between North America and Siberia. However, since the seal is a mammal they were much closer to human beings than their fishy relatives, and there are innumerable tales of their interbreeding with humans. Some of the seal-people even seem to have had limited shape-shifting abilities, allowing them to assume a more human form when they wished. In Scotland they were known as *selkies*, as in the famous ballad *The Great Selkie of Sule Skerry*:

'I am a man upon the land,
And I'm a selkie in the sea
And when I'm far and far frae land,
My home it is in Sule Skerry.'

A great many unexpected pregnancies were explained away by the story of a particularly alluring selkie, so it is hard to say just how true all these accounts really are. But it is an enduring tradition that the great clan Macleod is descended from the selkies – and there are worse ancestors to have. They come down to us as a remote, rather sad people, and that is probably how our ancestors saw the last of them. Maybe they foresaw the fashion for sealskin coats.

The last race of water-elementals was wholly human, and looked much like their inland cousins the Rusalki. They had little use for the

The merfolk could be as attractive and as sinister as the sea itself. This mermaid seems to evoke the darker, stormier side of their nature, as does the weird seahorse overleaf. There were shapechangers among the seapeoples also, and this, challenging the power of the waves themselves, is probably one of them.

well-developed swimming powers of the merfolk and the selkies, since they tended to live in relatively deep, still waters and seldom came to the surface. These Finnfolk, as the Scots called them, went further than almost any other elemental race in their imitation of human lifestyle. They built themselves great cities under the sea, vast glittering palaces studded with all the treasures of the ocean. Not surprisingly, they were well-inclined towards men. Men were providing all this free booty – literally dropping it out of the sky – and besides, they were entertaining creatures with pleasant-looking bodies . . . Fortunately the Finnfolk never had really close encounters with the ordinary run of humanity. They would have been *so* disillusioned. Occasionally, though, they would take a human guest or lover down to their sunken realm. Those who wanted to seem to have returned, but the Finnfolk were wary enough to deprive them of much of their memory of the kingdoms under the sea. Such men and women as came back could remember little beyond vague images of beauty and riches. The Bremen Transcript mentions the Finnfolk only in passing; the tales suggest that they could still be seen as late as the eighteenth century. Now that humanity is at last breaking into the final sanctuaries of the ocean, it is likely that they will follow their fellow-elementals, if they have not already done so. But who knows? Perhaps one or other of those persistent seekers of the Lost Continent will one day come across the ruins of a city beyond his wildest dreams . . .

THE GREEN PEOPLE

As we have already seen, some of the most powerful elementals were as thick as any number of short planks. Of course, not all the weaker ones were paragons of intelligence, either, but it does seem that the more powerful elementals found intelligence rather beneath them. After all, they had magic: humans could do their thinking for them, and if humans were good thinkers, then obviously it was an inferior quality anyway.

Elementals intelligent enough not to share this attitude were apparently rather drawn towards the human form, and made the best use of it when they had it. The Finnfolk are one example, but another is

While their fellows struggled to take physical form, the older and wiser earth elementals watched the beautiful planet below them and considered the brief span of life allotted to humankind. Seeing men and women wither and grow old, they looked instead for a slower, stronger, and more enduring existence – and found it among the ancient forests. There the first of the green people took earthly form – and for thousands of years the forests of the world were theirs.

just as impressive – and startlingly recent.

Many earth elementals sculpted themselves bodies out of stone or clay – the original *golems* of Jewish mythology – but others chose more promising material, already alive but simple and tractable. The trees that took their mineral food from deep within the earth made ideal homes for elementals of modest size and aspirations, and many of them settled in as the dryads and 'tree-folk' of classical legend. Many were

In the past people saw tree-spirits as beautiful, ethereal creatures, whereas today science fiction seems to be obsessed with malignant triffid-like creatures. In fact, the tree people seem to have been both; serene and beautiful if undisturbed, they could become monstrous if threatened.

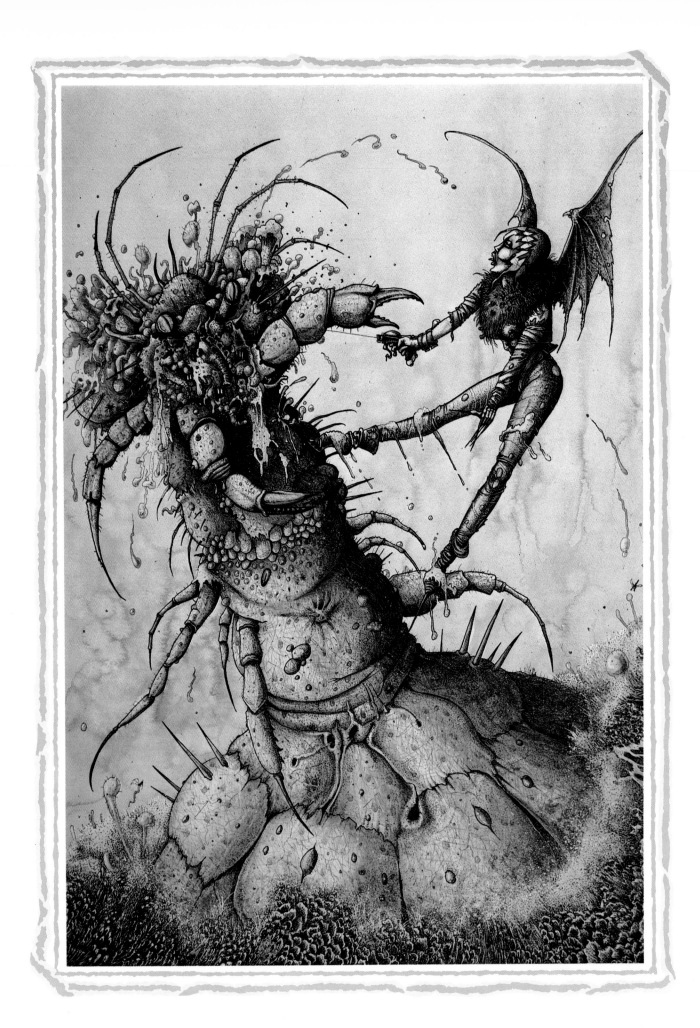

content to remain as they were, shadowy creatures dependent on their home, unable to move far from it, and fleeing back to it at the slightest sign of danger. They shared the ups and downs of their home tree – even when it was cut down by ill-mannered humans, who were regarded with the same general love and esteem as modern real estate developers. Other elementals, more ambitious, were continually testing the limits of their living shells, using their powers to refine and alter the rough, slow vegetable metabolism. Within a few centuries they had turned it into a close analogue of a mammalian body. Specialized sap flowed almost as readily as blood through wide veins, and vegetable fibers that could brace massive tree-limbs against a northern gale stretched and tautened like human muscles. Like – but far stronger.

Some trees began to change shape, to sweep branches around independently of the wind, to twitch their roots in the soil as though they itched to be up and walking. Some began using their new bodies as a disguise to prey on humans. Unsuspecting forest-dwellers would be struck dead by the sweep of a well-aimed branch and hastily buried to enrich the soil around the killer's roots. But sooner or later they would be discovered, and retribution would be swift and final. Other elementals resorted to subtler, more alarming tactics. The Greeks knew the cypress tree as the thief of intelligence, a vampire of the mind. Its cool shade was very inviting on a blazing summer day, but if you picked the wrong tree for your siesta you were liable to wake up with your mind drained as clear of memories as a new-born baby's. In England the oak and the holly, especially the 'barren' male holly, developed the same sinister reputation. Trees learned fast that way.

Some tree spirits, like the Slavic Leshy, were less malevolent. They preferred practical jokes, such as leading lone travellers miles out of their way and then scaring the daylights out of them. If you have a face the colour of fungoid wood, a green, mossy beard, and staring green eyes, and the rest of you is mostly tree, this is none too difficult.

The tree people in our prehistoric forests were still nightmarish outlines, with no clear hands or fingers on their great limbs. Instead there might be a cluster of small flexible branches that writhed shut round whatever they grasped, careless of cracked twigs and shredded leaves. There were no clearly-defined joints: the massive body could not bend further than a wind-blown tree without splitting its barky skin and eventually snapping. As a rule the tree people lived apart, long and slowly, coming together once in a few decades. But as the centuries passed they were driven closer together, for mutual protection, by the forest's new enemy: man, and his murdering servant, fire. Primitive

In the old days the woods were the living calendar of the seasons, embodied in the growth and fall of the leaves. Around the wood and in the shadow of its branches men and women lived out their everyday lives. But were all the figures that moved through the glades people? The wood sheltered more than mere human life; strange voices were heard in the thickets, odd battles were fought in the copses, peculiar creatures crept towards lonely cottages. And eerie life stirred in the trees themselves; or was it just the wind that muttered in the branches? But now man makes a bare and treeless world (overleaf), a wilderness of rotting roots where only skeletal birds find nests.

155

man's early farming – aptly named 'slash-and-burn' cultivation – bit deeper into the natural world every spring. Any tree spirit unable to up roots and run for it when he saw a human farmer coming would be just one more log on the fire; though even being a dryad in the woodpile may have been better than ending up as the farmer's walls, or, worse yet, his furniture. The tree people liked to remain in one spot as far as possible, but when the merry singing of yet another party of woodcutters and charcoal-burners echoed through the wood they would flit away into the dim depths of the forest, where man did not dare to follow – yet. There they settled in glades with their surviving fellows.

Not surprisingly, humans came to fear these glades. The defence tactics employed by the last of the tree people were various, but always highly effective. Those survivors from older generations who had not adopted the fashion for human-like bodies still looked exactly like trees – old trees with only a few branches left – so it was hardly surprising if a

A dryad, chased by an over-eager human suitor, about to take refuge in 'her' tree. Already her hands, meshing with its outer branches, are being reunited with the twigs from which they were made, while her graceful body arches in towards the trunk whose shape it echoes. Her face has assumed the age-old dryad expression of mingled fear and eagerness that occasionally caused even the gods to forget themselves. The Greek god Apollo was one, and his vigorous pursuit of the dryad Daphne could have only one conclusion. Later stories have tended to assume that Daphne was an ordinary nymph, miraculously transformed into a laurel after her impassioned prayer to Artemis, goddess of virgins. It seems far more likely that she was a flirting laurel-spirit who took the game just a little too far.

159

human woodman made the mistake of laying his axe to such a promising-looking trunk. The tree-man would usually return the favour. Fortunately, as we gather from fairy-tales, the world was never short of new woodcutters. The original dryads probably began their lives as a new adaptation for survival. It isn't easy to cut down a tree that has a disturbing similarity to a beautiful girl, still less easy if it appears to be making an effort to seduce you. But the dryads were very much in the minority. In general human beings thought of these glades as the haunt of uneasy, ambiguous spirits such as the Green Man, embodying the lurking, watchful power of the ancient trees. Many early human religions, such as the worship of Artemis at Ephesus and the Norse cult of Odin, began by offering sacrifice – usually human sacrifice – in these sacred groves. Once, perhaps, the sacrifices had been accepted, though not by the gods they were intended for. The gods had better things to do. However, even the mildest-natured tree creature could always use a little extra soil enrichment.

Many tree people, though, developed a more tolerant attitude towards human beings. Perhaps they had learned something from all those drained memories. They admired human bodies, respected human brains, and did their best to live with human faults and failings. Over the centuries they came to look more and more like men – when it suited them – and some were positively friendly to mankind, notably the later and more mobile descendants of those early dryads. Their line in teasing was spectacularly original: it's more than a little disconcerting to find a silver birch bending gently to the breeze in the thicket where you've just trapped a delightful wood-nymph. The lordly Tapio, the Finnish forest divinity, was a far more powerful figure, dark, austere, but basically benevolent, as long as his realm was treated with proper respect. He is well portrayed in Sibelius' famous tone-poem *Tapiola*. But even he drew the line somewhere, and foolish woodcutters tempted by that really enormous pine in the exact centre of the forest vanished quietly and without fuss, leaving at most a battered woollen cap dangling idly on the tip of a low bough. Tapio, with his mixture of benevolence and danger, was very probably the model for the ents in *The Lord of the Rings* – if it wasn't the ents themselves, that is.

Medieval man often glimpsed elusive, leaf-cloaked forms in the deep forest shadow, and imagined them as some kind of human savage, like the ones he had heard about in southern lands. 'Wild men', or woses, as they were known, were regarded with patronizing interest. In fact, they became a common theme in medieval art, and frequently appear as heraldic supporters on coats of arms, holding up the emblems of the nobility. By that time, though, they were rare. The Great Retreat had swept up most of the tree people still surviving after man's incursions into the woods. And some, again like Tolkien's ents, had simply become tree-like again, sleeping a long sleep until fire, axe, wind, or lightning took them off. Some still lingered in the as yet

Some of the green folk started small, inhabiting plants and shrubs. But charming as these little creatures were, they found it hard to abide being gardened. Some gave up, and moved to the smaller trees; one or two, though, are still to be found in the better botanical gardens.

undisturbed North American forests, in the rain forests of South America, the jungles of Africa, and the great hill forests of the East, but everywhere they were being beaten back. In North America they enjoyed a brief respite between the arrival of the Vikings, who had come looking for timber, and the coming of the southern Europeans a few hundred years later. The Amerinds preferred to live in and by the forest,

as a rule, rather than cut it down. The tree people tolerated this attitude as the best that they could expect, since the Indians saw the forest as the dwelling of a great *manitou*, a power of nature best treated with respect, and kept their clearing and burning to a minimum. With the flood of immigrants from Europe, the tree people lost their final sanctuary. In South America they lost ground to rubber plantations and the ruthless

Above: Cobweb, Moth, Peaseblossom, and Mustardseed: Arthur Rackham's interpretation of four of the fairies from Shakespeare's Midsummer Night's Dream. *It is likely that creatures rather similar to these prettified flower fairies were among the early ancestors of the taller, stronger, and infinitely more sinister tree peoples who turned the medieval forest into a place of mystery and darkness. Opposite: A tinker takes his ease beneath the tangled roots of an old oak tree, unaware of the danger that awaits him should he fall asleep. Tree people in the form of oaks were reputed to be vampires of the mind.*

ROGER WEBB '79

logging of land-hungry farmers and they, too, joined the Retreat or perished as they stood.

In Europe they had long been extinct. But as late as the 12th century the tree people made a curious reappearance. The English chroniclers Ralph of Coggeshall and William of Newbridge both record the strange appearance of two children in a pit near St Mary's of the Wolf-Pits in Suffolk. They were apparently human, but green-skinned, able to eat like humans, but totally vegetarian. The boy soon died, but the girl survived, and eventually lost the green tinge in her skin and became acclimatized to human foods. The only account she gave of her origin was that she and her brother came from a strange twilit world where all the people were green-skinned; attracted by the sound of church bells, the two children had strayed out through a cavern and been unable to find their way back. There is little doubt that these were dryad children of late, more or less humanoid stock: there are several telling clues. Firstly, the vegetarian preference. As the sacrifices showed, the tree people could eat meat, but preferred not to. They found it harder to digest. Secondly, the green skin. The dryad metabolism was by now very similar to the human, but still partly based on chlorophyll. In the caverns described in the account they would have needed a greater concentration of chlorophyll near the skin surface than they did in the full light of day. Perhaps that was what killed the boy; but the girl, possibly younger, was able to adjust more easily. Thirdly, she lived for a long time, and was recorded as being 'rather loose and wanton in her habits'. In other words, she had the dryad's traditionally unfettered attitude to sex. But despite all this activity, she never had any children – not one. That, given the other resemblances, is the clincher. The human resemblance of the tree people could be very strong – but in the last analysis, it was never more than bark-deep.

WITCHES

The elementals' final attempt to strike back against humanity caused a great deal of trouble and an unpleasant amount of bloodshed. But it was hardly a slaughter on the scale of the Titan Wars, and the elementals responsible for it were in no way the equals of the gods of old. In fact they were the last, slowest, and least gifted remnants of their kind, left behind in the wake of the Great Retreat. For some reason many of them congregated in the British Isles. Here they worked what rather feeble mischief they were capable of. Like their distant cousins, the vampires, they were air elementals. Unable to construct bodies of their own, they entered the physical world by worming their way into the bodies of

The European witch-cults worshipped demonaic figures at their Sabbat orgies, personifications of the evil in which they were guiltily revelling. Witches seem to have been willing to do almost anything to win their Masters' favour, the more stupid and degrading the better. And yet for all their satanic majesty, these imposing creatures don't seem to have achieved much. They couldn't even save their followers from witchfinders and other killjoys. Why?

other living creatures. The possession of human beings was far beyond their power, though; domestic animals and small birds were about their limit. Their commonest victims were dogs, cats, hedgehogs, owls, and rats, though in extreme cases they might be reduced to animating flies and spiders.

Yet even this half-witted crew kept some of their magic powers, if only because they desperately wanted to use them against what they saw as their greatest enemy: mankind. Everything that was wrong with the world could be laid at the door of that monstrous and imperialist aggressor, who should never have been allowed to come down out of the trees in the first place. Prometheus and the titans had a lot to answer for. . . Like all really spectacular failures, the left-over elementals could never believe that their miserable condition was due to their own inadequacy, and nothing else. In their view everything was the fault of humanity. Things had been allowed to slip too far. It was time to teach them a lesson.

They began to think this way around the time Stonehenge was built. It took them until the Middle Ages to work out what to do, and until the 16th or in some cases the 17th century to summon up the nerve to do it. Meanwhile that arrogant aggressor, man, continued to build up his so-called civilisation, blissfully unaware that he was oppressing anybody except, perhaps, his fellow-man. Little did he know that the great elemental conspiracy was at last (after a few thousand years) ready to be put into action.

Unsurprisingly, the great conspiracy showed an appalling lack of

"Horse and Hattock!" cry the witches in an old folk-tale as they fly off to their Sabbat; the unfortunate traveller who copies them gets borne along behind. Rackham's illustration to the tale shows the witches led by their familiars, who have taken the form of scrawny cats, and he is probably not too far from the truth. The elemental familiars had little power left to them, but it is likely enough that they provided their worshippers with a joyride from time to time.

At the witches' Sabbat animal masks were sometimes used, both as a disguise and to symbolize the bestiality of the passions to be unleashed. But few, if any, animals ever managed to be quite as stupid as the humans who fell for the witchcults or the superannuated elementals who organized them. Useful as they found them, the trollwitches such as this one who originally employed the familiars knew just how little they could be trusted. You never found a troll leaping naked round a fire, lapping bats' blood; stupid they were, but there **were** limits.

imagination. The elementals' experience of life and the world in general had not really prepared them for the task of overthrowing the dominant species. At one time a few of them had earned a precarious living by hiring themselves out to troll-shamans as spies, eavesdroppers, messenger-boys, and sentinels. Their speciality had been guard duty on files of secret spells and formulae, a job where brains were more of a liability than an asset. For a while it was quite common to see an old troll-witch with an owl perched on her wrist and a mouse balanced on her shoulder, apparently whispering into her ear. The slow-moving trolls had many uses for small, rapid scouts who saw much and thought little, though naturally they were careful not to offend their little

servants by telling them so. Unfortunately this gave the elementals a grossly inflated idea of their own importance: and it was this misconception that was finally, after all those centuries, coming home to roost.

Somewhere, somehow, the elementals had got hold of the idea that they had been the 'power behind the throne' in the troll-tribes. This being so, the way to take revenge on the human race was obviously to use the same technique to worm their way into the confidence of the people in power. Their magic was not as strong as it might be – even *they* knew that – but a little went a long way among humans.

It might almost have worked. At least, it might have done if the elementals had had any real understanding of mankind. Unfortunately their ideas were several centuries out of date. Humanity had not been relying on the services of shamans and witches for quite some time, except in outlying village communities. There were priests, of course, not to mention doctors and alchemists; but any small animal that tried to strike up a conversation with a priest risked at the least being drenched with holy water, and if he wasn't careful (and many weren't) being roasted alive. The doctors and alchemists were still using medieval formularies and spell-books, so they should have been more amenable. In fact a talking animal was likely to find itself on the dissecting table somewhere in the middle of its second sentence, while its intended victim hunted enthusiastically through its vitals in case the Philosopher's Stone happened to be hidden in there somewhere. If not, the liver and tongue could always be sold 'myxed with a little antimonie and mummy-paste, a most certaine remedie agaynste ye dumbnesse ...'

As it happened, very few of the elementals had the imagination to attempt contact with priests or alchemists. Most of them were still under the impression that the village was the most important human

community, and the shaman or witch the most influential person in the village. It was true, of course, that village life had changed very little, and most could still point to an old woman (or, more rarely, an old man) who dispensed bad advice, useless love-potions, and rather more efficient poisons. A little assistance from an elemental, even a fourth-rate elemental, did wonders for the professional reputation of such a walking relic, especially in the poisons and curses department. But after a few hundred years or so even the slowest of these low-grade familiars began to realise that they were nowhere near the real human power

Most witches's familiars took the form of small animals of one kind or another – cats and toads were commonest, but snakes and foxes and bats were also popular, along with the occasional hedgehog. The more frightening forms were less easy to keep around the house, but they did have a few advantages; they were very good for frightening off witchfinders and similar busybodies, especially with a little special effects work on the side. That was really about all these degenerate elementals were capable of.

centres. Things needed stirring up a little. And so they goaded on their human agents to organize secret cults, using orgiastic rites as a bait. At such gatherings a dozen or more elementals would join together, straining all their magic to create a monstrous (if rather insubstantial) form that their human dupes would see as the Devil. By a combination of fear, greed, and illicit pleasure the uneducated and the credulous were bound to the service of the cult; and no doubt it gave the elementals a good deal of amusement to see human beings making such spectacular fools of themselves with so little prompting from their would-be conquerors.

Fortunately the damage done by these cults was in proportion to the small-minded malice of their creators. Despite the awful-sounding oaths and the would-be blasphemous rites, the people foolish enough to be taken in by the elementals were rarely capable of more than petty mischief, low cunning, and general unpleasantness. The depths of evil were as far beyond them as the heights of intelligence. In any case, there were never very many elemental familiars. Most of the little pets kept by lonely old women were no more than pets, though sometimes both pet and owner suffered horrible tortures for the sins of the few real witches and their elemental companions. There is no need to document the horrors of the sixteenth and seventeenth century witch-hunts. The details are all too readily available for those who want them. But the elementals' part in beginning it all is less well-known, and their motives are hardly known at all. Perhaps if they were, those painfully respectable suburbanites who delight in prancing naked round undersized bonfires (or conducting detailed and embarrassing rites in chalk pentacles drawn on the garage floor) would think better of it. Somewhere, after all, a particularly dim-witted elemental is laughing its head off.

ELVES

One of the more interesting questions left unanswered by the text of the Transcript is the identity of the mysterious stranger the *ephor* mentions in the opening sentences of the first quoted folio. It is hinted that this is not a human being, yet from the one or two brief mentions of him later in the text he seems to have been curiously reluctant to discuss his origins. Nor, in this case, is the information supposedly given by the titan Corineus any more helpful. One line suggests that the stranger's people were descended from air elementals; another that they had always, as far as anyone knew, inhabited physical bodies. From the brief description of the stranger we gather that these bodies were much

Evil sprites tumble out of Pandora's Box to bring misery to humankind: the story as illustrated by Arthur Rackham. Although Greek legends tells us that the gods ensured the release of such horror into the world by entrusting the sealed box containing it to poor, curiosity-ridden humanity, it sounds more like the work of the dark elves. The unseelie court had no love of the human race, and it would be like them to play upon human weaknesses to achieve their ends.

like human ones, but far better constructed: larger, handsomer, stronger, and proof against the ravages of age and illness. Very few of them seem to have lived in southern lands. A casual reference in the Transcript places them 'in the Hyperborean lands', the countries above the North Wind – in other words, northern Europe. Apparently they lived aloof and distant from humankind, and from their fellow-elementals. One of the few definite things Corineus is quoted as saying about them is that they lived in a kind of semi-feudal society, divided into a series of courts, but subject to the authority of two great Courts. One of these was well disposed towards mankind; the other most definitely was not. The Transcript's truncated description of them slides between awe and terror. It seems that they were basically a noble race, but passionate, wilful, and very dangerous to cross.

We have been told just enough. Scottish folklore records the tales of the 'seelie' and 'unseelie' courts, and a race central to Scandinavian mythology is divided into two peoples, those of light, and those of the dark: the *ljösalfar* and the *svartalfar*. The word *alfar* is the origin of the English word *elves*.

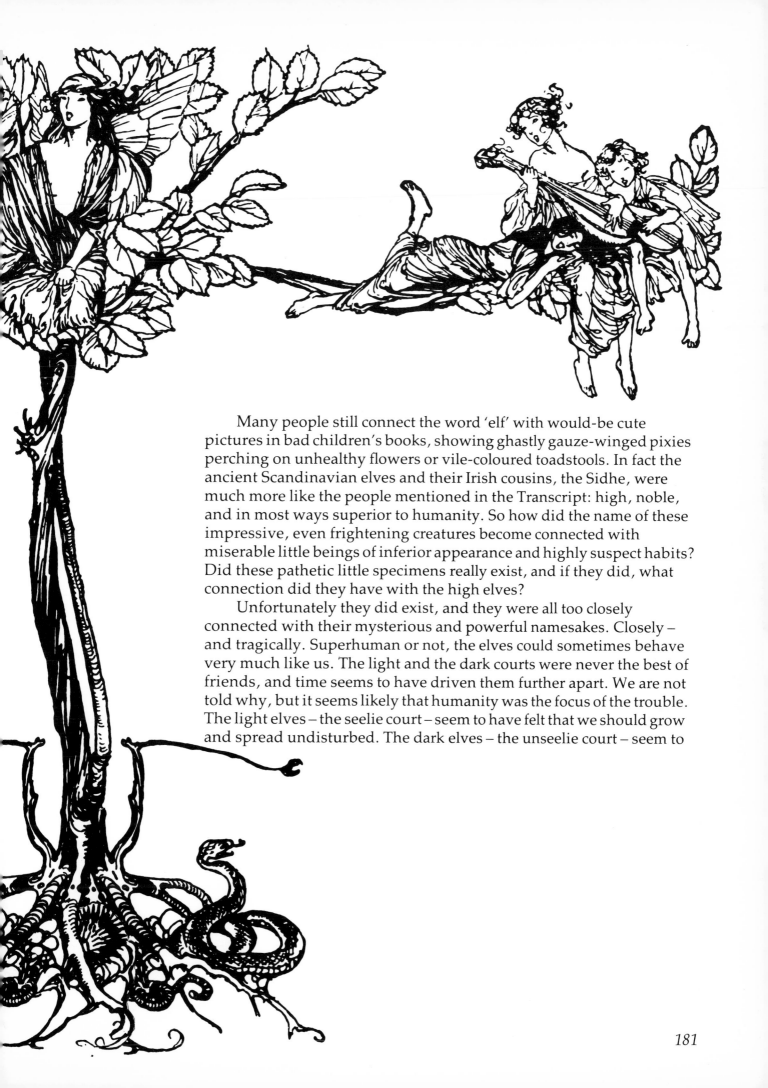

Many people still connect the word 'elf' with would-be cute pictures in bad children's books, showing ghastly gauze-winged pixies perching on unhealthy flowers or vile-coloured toadstools. In fact the ancient Scandinavian elves and their Irish cousins, the Sidhe, were much more like the people mentioned in the Transcript: high, noble, and in most ways superior to humanity. So how did the name of these impressive, even frightening creatures become connected with miserable little beings of inferior appearance and highly suspect habits? Did these pathetic little specimens really exist, and if they did, what connection did they have with the high elves?

Unfortunately they did exist, and they were all too closely connected with their mysterious and powerful namesakes. Closely – and tragically. Superhuman or not, the elves could sometimes behave very much like us. The light and the dark courts were never the best of friends, and time seems to have driven them further apart. We are not told why, but it seems likely that humanity was the focus of the trouble. The light elves – the seelie court – seem to have felt that we should grow and spread undisturbed. The dark elves – the unseelie court – seem to

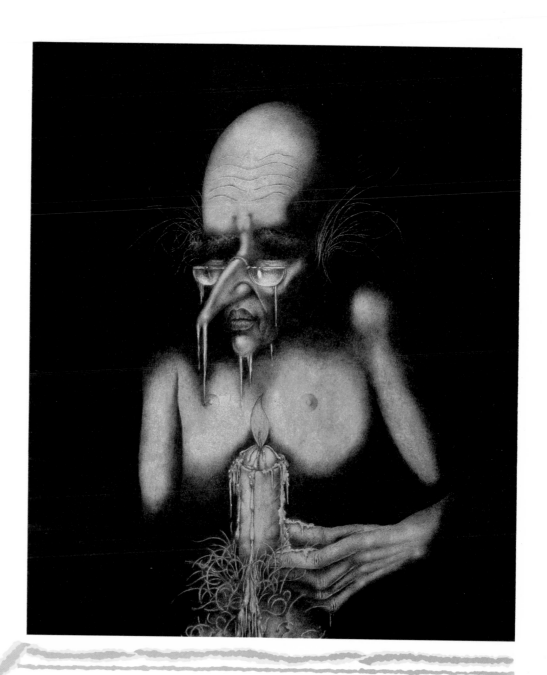

Opposite: Elves, as most people think of them — quaint, undersized, feeble, with pointed ears and cute bug eyes, creatures at home with snails, insects and other lowly animals. And yet, debased as it is, there is still a hint of sinister power here. What's in that package? And what do they need the space for? Baby-stealing, leaving a changeling instead, was an old habit of the Unseelie Court, and one they were slow to give up. Above: They had other nasty habits, too, including spiteful tricks like the will-o'the-wisp, or elf-candle. This, shown with disgusting accuracy here, would appear in marshes at night to lead travellers off the safe paths.

have had other plans. Perhaps it is as well we know nothing of them. The situation had close parallels with that in America just before the Civil War, with humanity cast in the role of the blacks. The result was much the same. A catastrophic war was fought, using powers that had not been unleashed since the first elemental battles. At the end of it both the great Courts had been shattered, and their people were scattered across the face of the earth: those that were left alive. Most were dead, and many of the rest were strangely warped and weakened. The unseelie court had suffered the most: only a few of its people remained, their bodies and their powers stunted, shrivelled, and diminished to the point where they had little power to harm us. Of the seelie court

Opposite: A conventional image of the elves, another drawing by Arthur Rackham. The juxtaposition of the grotesque pixie figure, with its long nose and pointed ears, and the doll-like fairy behind it, is familiar in most of the later stories and pictures of the degenerate high eleves. It seems almost impossible that these creatures could once have held such enormous power. Surviving descriptions, notably from Cornwall, suggest that the more formidable members of the unseelie court were often accompanied by powerful and sinister bodyguards, known to the Cornishmen as spriggans. Though shrunken like the other elves, spriggans had enough magic to call up an illusion of their former power and size to frighten away intruders. As for the pretty little elf behind the spriggan, she may not be all she seems. The Danes still tell how elf-women never turn their backs on a human being – because they are like empty husks, hollow, and without true substance. All their beauty is no more than a mask, a means of luring human beings to their doom, or snatching them out of time into the otherworld.

more had survived but they, too, were severely weakened, and most seem to have joined the Great Retreat with the rest of the secret peoples. A few of their war casualties, as stunted as their opponents, were left behind; but all that had made them high elves had been destroyed.

The war cannot be dated, but it seems to have taken place only a few hundred years before the Transcript was originally set down: it was still a vivid memory to Numenos' informants. Folklore suggests that the last of the high elves vanished before the year 1000, so there is some excuse for such later writers as Shakespeare (notably in *A Midsummer Night's Dream*) attaching the name 'elf' to the wizened remants of the elder courts. In stories they survive as imps, goblins, and brownies, occasionally helpful to humans, but more often mischievous or downright dangerous in a rather petty way. It is a sad come-down for a once great people – and a lesson that humanity would do well to remember. We have the power to fight a war at least as destructive as theirs; and if we did, who would even remember *our* name?

DEMONS

Demons, as such, were not one of the secret peoples. In fact they had no existence at all outside learned books. The willingness of certain authorities, notably the medieval church, to see these creatures at every turn was due to their inability to understand the true nature of the elementals. Anything that was not human tended to be loosely labelled as a 'demon', whether it was a giant, a god, a troll, a dwarf, or a merman. The word might almost be described as a term of political abuse like 'Leftist' or 'Fascist', that may once have had a clear and definable meaning but has been debased by years of misuse into meaning nothing more than 'someone who does not share my point of view'.

The classic image of a demon: a hellish horned figure with the ears of a goat dripping venom from tusked and gaping jaws. Visions like this one, used by the last surviving elementals to inspire the 16th and 17th century witch-cults, was created out of dim memories of trolls and semi-humans of an earlier age.

There is no doubt that the occasional appearance of elementals in the Middle Ages must have been very alarming to churchmen in particular, but there is no need to suppose that we are dealing with a separate race, and the Transcript sheds no light on them. It is possible that the fire elementals, always the most elusive of the secret peoples, may have made a number of more or less spectacular appearances at that time; if they had they would inevitably have been connected with the popular image of the Devil, soon to be taken up and fostered by the elemental-inspired witch cults. But there is no need to assume it. One doubts whether a country priest confronted by an elemental would have stopped to check on its precise physical and material makeup before running for dear life. He, after all, was only *human*.

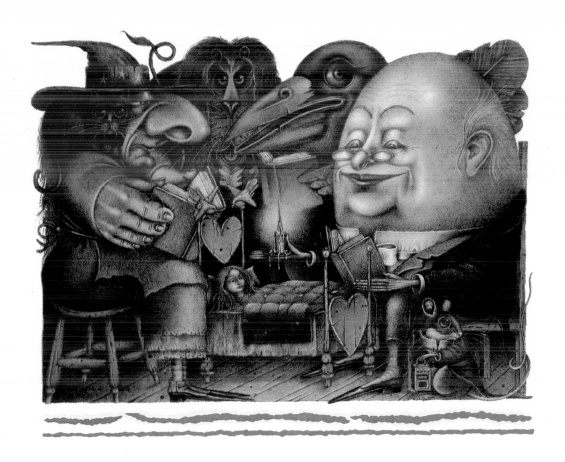

ACKNOWLEDGEMENTS

All B/W line drawings in the text are by Arthur Rackham apart from those on Pages 49, 104, 105, 172, 173 which are by Rita Renella.